Cover illustration by
Mathias Schädlich

HUMAN ENERGY

An analysis of the human energy field

HUMAN ENERGY

Published by

Douglas Barry Publications

Holborn Gate
1st Floor, 330 High Holborn
London
WC1V 7QT
ENGLAND

Tel 020 7872 5745
Fax 020 7753 2824
E-mail info@DougasBarry.com

FIRST PUBLISHED IN THE U.K. 2005

HUMAN ENERGY

COPYRIGHT 2005
©Douglas Barry Publications

British Library - A CIP Catalogue
record for this book is available
from the British Library.

I.S.B.N.   0-9540176-7-6

Dedication

This book is dedicated to Ellen Clarke, a wonderful energy healer.

Acknowledgements

This book is the synthesis of many years of experience working with human energy; practising energy healing in various forms, and teaching workshops. The ideas in this book began a number of years ago, when I was asked to teach a short workshop on human energy, for some recently qualified therapists. I would like to thank Renee Tanner, Barry and BJ, for their encouragement and support throughout the years.

I would also like to thank artist Mathias Schädlich for the cover illustration, some of the other art work found in the book, and for *taming the tiger* during the writing of this book.

My thanks would not be complete without mentioning my teachers, mentors and friends who have shared their knowledge, experiences and expertise with me: Ellen Clarke, Stuart R. Hilda Holyman, Karen H., Sarah W., Deb C., Janis, Bobbie, Katrina McNabb, Jean Glen, Berni & Doreen from Whitley Bay…to mention but a few.

Special thanks to Marie for letting me loose with her aura photo and to Mark Haeffner, for proof reading my original script.

Note to the Reader

This book is not intended as a substitute for professional or medical advice.

Neither the author nor publisher can accept any responsibility whatsoever for any health problem which results from the use of the methods described in this book.

The reader is urged to consult a general medical practitioner as to the cause or nature of a health problem of any sort.

CONTENT

Human Energy   by   Dr Jarrod Hollis

Why Study Human Energy?

You might ask the question, why study human energy? What's the issue here? Actually in the West this would be quite a viable question. Nevertheless, today there is an increasing number of complementary therapies that are being practiced that are based on energy: for example, reiki, spiritual healing, reflexology, some forms of holistic massage, aura soma, Indian head massage, shiatsu, acupuncture, qi gong, acupressure, ayuveda, magnetic healing, to mention just a few. The point is that in order to appreciate these therapies fully, one needs to understand their roots, and for all of these therapies, the root is human energy; the form it takes, how this effects a persons well being. All of these therapies view human energy in subtly different ways drawing on different cultural explanations for their base. All of these different approaches might seem very different, and certainly it is no wonder that people who are new to the area find the information difficult to follow. On closer examination what seems like disparate theories relate quite closely to one another.

The Body as a Cosmos

From a Western perspective, the human body comprises of physical structures, such as organ, tissues, fluids and vessels, that function together as body systems. This efficiency of this functioning determines ones health and well being. This is the dominant view in the West, and forms the medical model of health. Indeed, this perspective has become the dominant view in the modern world.

In most other traditional views of health the body is seen as a cosmos, or miniature universe that mirrors the environment. This might seem like a strange idea at first, but actually it is very simple.
Any physical structures in the world (in nature, the environment or indeed our body) are made up of particles, and atoms. The basis of

these atoms and particles are energetic in nature. This is explained further in the chapter that follows. So it would seem that in many ways, the human body is no different to other items of the physical world, except that man has consciousness.

Viewing all of the physical world as energy allows one to consider the body and the harmony between man and nature (the environment). It also allows one to consider internal harmony, within the human body itself. In this way the interdependence of the whole body systems, the physical structures and the mind, are acknowledged. Due to the interdependence of the whole body the inter relationships between the different organs and body systems are of great importance. The interdependence and interrelationships also provide a very good account of psychological well being, and identify the effects of thoughts and emotions on the physical body.

If one considers any culture in history, one can find man and the universe as a unity, depicted in many cultural symbols. Indeed, these symbols appear in art and ritual. One of the most powerful of these symbols is the mandala, and its many guises. Mandala's appear in almost every cultural system; Islam, Christianity, Hinduism and Buddhism. The mandala is a concentric symbol that is thought to reflect the shape of the universe, showing the inter-relationships, and the cyclic nature of the cosmos.

So, two principle questions are posed by this book. First, what is subtle human energy? Second, how have the different cultures described and characterised the human energy systems? The following chapters provide some of the answers to these questions.

The first chapter considers how the individual thinks about and perceives subtle energies. The chapters that follow present how a number of different ancient cultural systems have described and characterised human energy and the way that this energy flows through the physical body. Finally, the last chapter provides a synthesis of these ideas, and considers how Western new age ideas can be moulded and enhanced with the traditional views to form a new energy theory that we have termed *Renbardou*. Each section of this book starts with a hand painted mandala, as a symbol that each theory or culture provides a different description and account of what is fundamentally the same thing: *subtle human energy*.

What is Human Energy?

What do we mean by Human Energy?

There has always been a belief in the concept of a *"vital energy"* that supplies and surrounds the human body. Such ideas were present in most of the ancient civilisations, such as ancient Egypt, India, Greece and Rome. By the late eighteenth century Mesmer, conducted a number of studies to try and characterise what was meant by this *vital* energy. Numerous explanations have been proposed, and today, there is a myriad of ideas. At first sight, all of these ideas seem disparate, however on further examination one can identify striking similarities in how the energy has been characterised. The material in this book is an attempt to characterise some of these ideas and provide a synthesis.

If we look at any standard dictionary we can find a definition of energy. This one was found in a Readers Digest dictionary from 1974:

Energy: n. 1. Force, vigour (of speech, action, person etc); active operation; power actively exerted, (pl.) individual powers in exercise; capacity to produce effect. 2. (physics) Power of doing work possessed at any instant by a body or system of bodies; *actual kinetic* – body's power of work by virtue of stresses resulting from its relation to other bodies; *mass* – energy which all bodies possess in virtue of their mass, and of which a small portion is released (as radiations etc.) in radioactivity and other types of disintegration; *conservation of* – principle that the total of any closed system of bodies(including the universe) is invariable.

If you consult a thesaurus, you will find even more attributes and associations with energy. These were the synonyms for energy found in Collins Essential Thesaurus, 1988:
Energy: activity, animation, efficacy, efficiency, force, intensity, life, manliness, pluck, power, spirit, strength, strenuousness, vigour, zeal.

As you can see there are a large number of ideas presented in these definitions. What they convey *descriptors* or attributes of our experiences of energy, but they don't really give us much information about *what* human energy is. So, the first question that needs to be answered is what do we mean by energy, and how does the average person perceive and experience energy? Certainly there are many hundreds of new age books, that describe energy in many different ways, but how do these relate to people's own personal experiences?

This question became a topic of investigation for myself and Renée Tanner. We were concerned that many people studying complementary therapies that were supposed to be based on energy, often had very little background knowledge of energy; what it was and how it was maintained, and how it might be manipulated in the clinical setting. So our first aim was to characterise energy and investigate what peoples' own thoughts and feelings were on the topic. We also very interested to see how people actually perceived what they term "subtle energies".

The first study that follows involved interviewing two groups of people about what they understood by the term "human energy". A group of experienced practitioners' were asked this question, and their responses were compared to the responses from a group of people who had just started learning about complementary therapy.

The responses were subjected to a qualitative analysis and produced quite striking similarities.

Interpretive analysis of the question "What is Energy"?

A large number of responses reflected dictionary explanations of the word energy. This can be seen in the use of terms such as "force".

The word *universal* was also a commonly given descriptor as an explanation.
For example:

"What we and everything in the universe is made up of."

"Universal energy (life force) which parades all things. The power of life"

Many of the explanations given by the respondents also contained some kind of reference to the idea that energy has momentum, and that human energy is cyclic and one with nature:

"Energy is fundamentally what we are and is constantly changing with the world".

"Flow of nature, runs between everything".
It's a force that flows through the body and through all living things

There were also a number of references that link energy, thoughts and consciousness. For example,

"a manifestation of consciousness influenced by thought"

On a number of occasions, terms derived from existing energy explanations us were given. Nevertheless, when asked to elaborate, even the experienced therapists had difficulty in explaining what they actually meant. They often just gave other alternative terms as an explanation. For example:

"Energy is Chi in my understanding.......Vital force, life energy, chi, dynamism...... channels in the body.....prana"

Many of the respondents indicated that energy could be perceived as having both a positive and negative aspect:

"Positive and negative energy can unbalance people and influence their well being

".....it can be draining or empowering".

"....there's environment that gives me a lot of energy and there are environments that take a lot as well....."

"...a good environment balances your own energy and a bad one creates imbalance.."

When posed with the question, "could the energy from the environment effect the individual", every respondent to say that yes, they believed that it could. The responses in this section were very interesting as they reflected how people can experience atmosphere in terms of both their social and environmental surroundings:

"People feel better in nature where there is pure energy. Sometimes I feel sick and tried when I go into Oxford St".

"Vibrations between people and atmosphere affect each other."

"Wave (microwaves) telegraph poles, all affect the natural surroundings".

"Electricity pylons"

"Twilight has a very peaceful effect on me"
"The sun gives me the type of energy that makes me feel happy, calm"

Finally, when posed with the question, could an individual use their energy to influence another person in any way, all respondents indicated that they believed that this was certainly the case:

"Yes, for example Reiki, the therapist passes energy to heal".

"Touch has a major impact on most people, calming, healing, reassuring".

"a calm person can calm an upset/tense person and vice-versa"

"Yes, individuals can channel energy - for good or for other purposes"
"Voodoo"

The first thing to note was that people (even those experienced therapists) found it quite difficult to verbalise what they considered human energy to be. Both the experienced complementary practitioners and the novices tended to draw on holistic explanations such as "everything" "universal energy" etc, but they found it difficult to pin down as to what they actually meant. They often referred this energy to consciousness, and also used words such as *Chi, Prana, Vibrations, Vital Essence and Universal Life force.* Certainly these are terms that are often branded about and so it is no surprise to find then emerging here. Nevertheless, it was clear that people found it difficult to characterise exactly what these terms actually meant, or the background to concepts such as *"Prana"*.

Secondly, when people were asked "can the environment affect your energy? It was apparent that people depicted the environment to have both positive and negative effects on an individuals' energy. For example, microwaves and electricity pylons were depicted as having negative effects on human energy, whereas countryside forests, and sunshine were depicted as having positive effects on human energy. The response to this question indicated a striking positive/negative divide.

Thirdly, when people were asked whether a person could affect change on someone else's energy, both positive and negative examples were given and this divide was again apparent. The novices often described how someone could give off positive energy to benefit other people, and the experienced therapists, indicated how someone could have both a positive and negative effect on another person.

Experiencing Energy

The second issue that we were interested in was how people actually experienced human energy. The group of people were asked to hold out their hands parallel to one another, and to experience energy flowing between the hands, for a few minutes. The group were asked to write down any sensations they experienced (if any). This is a simple exercise depicted in most Reiki and healing texts. The exercise is also commonly given at qi gong, shaitsu, and healing classes. These responses were subjected to content and thematic analysis.

In total 63 observations were recorded. Two of the people gave the response "nothing". 61 other descriptive words were given to the sensations. These words were categorised as follows:

Content analysis of the sensations experienced during the basic energy exercise

Word	% Occurrence as a Description
Heat or Warmth	44%
Density or Space	20%.
Pins and Needles/ Tingling	15%
Movement	5%
Electricity	5%
Coolness	5%
Calmness, Relaxation	3%
Other Sensations	3%

The most frequent response for the sensations was temperature: heat or coolness. Temperature accounted for almost half of all of the responses (44% heat, 5% coolness, total responses regarding temperature 49%). The next most popular response was sensations of space (20%) where people experienced what they described as a resistance or force occupying the space between the hands.

Many of the responses indicated that they person was experiencing something that they could not verbalise. Often a sensation of "something there", "a resistance" was as frequently given. This was followed by sensations of pins and needles or tingling sensations (15%).

The next part of our preliminary investigation was a series of semi-structured, open ended interviews. What became very apparent was that a very similar pattern of results emerged.

"Human energy....I would be thinking of it as a life force that..erm.. is fuelled by food and drink and that keeps us going. If I think of it in terms of what we give out in a different way, its more of what we give out...... it comprises....its em....god its hard to....vibrations I suppose".

"....I believe in positive and negative energy and things that fuel that kind of energy are thoughts and feelings.....
...so its kind of vibrations that you give off I think, either consciously or unconsciously and they have that effect...that effect is spread out to things in the universe".

People found it hard to verbalise their experiences, and often associated energy and consciousness. They often identified energy in terms of spiritual, mental and physical aspects.

The division between positive and negative balance and the individuals' energy being affected by the environment was also once again apparent:

"So I think that if you have good thoughts and good feelings and you direct it outwards... you can either direct them outwards deliberately to a particular person or the whole universe as people sometimes do. One form of that is prayer, witchcraft and stuff use a different form ermm...or you can do it unconsciousness you can feel negative or generally have a negative... say aura... but its as vague as energy. And that's going to unconsciously effect everything that you come into contact with".

What emerges from this research is that people have quite distinct ways in which they describe and perceive human energy. The majority of people who were asked felt something. All of the respondents indicated that they believed in energy in the environment and that this had the potential to effect individuals to some degree. It was clear that energy was depicted to have motion and to have both a negative and positive aspect.

Using the results of this investigation, how might we depict human energy? It would seem then that we can characterise the body energy in two principle ways: a) In terms of energy that the body manufactures and utilises in order to function and b) in terms of electromagnetic energy surrounding the atomic structure of each atom, molecule etc and surrounding the body as a whole. Both of these eventually make up the energy that surrounds and flows through the body.

In western approaches to health, we perceive the body comprises of a number of physical structures. These structures have specific functions and are interrelated in terms of the body's physiology. The body utilises energy converting carbohydrates that we consume and store in the body into ATP energy (e.g. Glycolysis within the cell) that the physical structures can use to function. When one considers the neurological system, this body system is based on the transport and passage of electrical activity. This electrical activity is essential to life.

Where does human energy come from?

In very simple terms, every structure is made up of atoms. Atoms consist of three basic particles, a proton, a neutron and an electron. The protons and electrons have a particular charge. Electrons orbit or circle the protons and electrons. Movement of the electrons liberates energy.

Atoms come together to form physical substance. So, our physical bodies are made up of molecules, tissues, organs etc, that all liberate electromagnetic energy. This energy surrounds our body and flows through the body.

According to some cultures our body energy also comprises of an energy component that is with us through out our lifetime. This has been described as universal energy that connects and nourishes all life. This energy has often been called many different names, such as *prana and Chi, Qi, or source*. Each culture views this energy or force is subtly different ways. Nevertheless, you will see in later chapters that these labels have very precise meanings and do not necessarily refer to such a general aspect of energy. These terms are clearly often miss-used and represented in general explanations of human energy. This is particularly true in complementary health practices. Nevertheless, some might view the inherited energy as "source".

Different Views on "Source"

Throughout history many names have been given to the concept of source energy: chi, orgone, esprit, loosh, prana, elan vital, and bio-electricity are just a few of these names and labels.

According to Taoist theory, Chi (Ki, Qi) originates from what is termed "*the source*". The source has also been called the Great Void, or emptiness and equivarlent concepts exist in other cultural systems. Taoists believe that the concept of Source is beyond human intellect. As one will see later when we consider Yin-yang theory energy is infinitely divisible. Therefore, Source can be sub divided. From Source we can form another abstract concept "The Myriad of Things", or all that we experience. At this point, energy condenses into the principle aspect of form, comprising of physical matter and energy. So one can see that although I have differentiated between energy

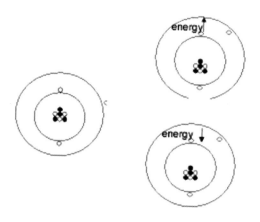

A Lithium Atom
The orbits are shown with two electrons in the inner orbit and one electron in the outer orbit. Sometimes the electons are required to move from one orbit to the other. This either requires energy or produces energy.

qualities produced by the physical body processes and source energy, these have originated from the same thing.
In other cultures, there is an equivalent view of "source". For example, in Indian (Hindu) cultures, source is the void or Om, and characterised as Kundali (more commonly and erroneously labelled Prana). The term Kundalini is derived from the Sanskrit meaning 'serpent energy'.

Hence, Kundalini is often portrayed as a serpent. Kundalini is the active energetic property, which functions under the direction of Universal Law. Kundalini has a function of recycling and directing life energy. Kundali has been characterised as a reservoir of creative energy and the foundation of our consciousness. This energy of consciousness lies dormant at the base of the spine, and is considered to be dormant unless activated through spiritual practice such as meditation or yoga. The power of Kundalini is claimed to be awesome and beyond description (note the similarity to the great void).

In the classical literature of Kashmir, Kundalini is described in three different forms. The first of these is as the universal para-kundalini. The second of these is a body-mind complex called prana-kundalini. The third of these is as consciousness form called shakti-kundalini which integrates the other two forms.

Nevertheless, what is being described in all of these is a spiritual aspect of energy, that is formed before birth and which provides a driving force, motivation and impetus for life. From this point I shall refer to this aspect as Source. You might think of life force energy as the energy that is part of our consciousness, or that which gives us our individual characteristics.

So, the "invisible" energy surrounds each human being and is comprised of an electromagnetic component, generated from the physical body and what I shall term a source component. The energy field integrally reflects the condition of the body and also affects the body by supporting the life process in all its aspects—the material operations of the physical body, the functions of the emotions and mind. The energy is also considered to relate to spiritual aspects of life.

How does "energy" effect the human body?

What we have learnt so far is that the bodies physical structure together with life force go together contribute to what we term "energy". It is no surprise then to find that the energy that surrounds the body reflects the inner state of being…how the physical, emotional and psychological aspects of the body are functioning. The energy surrounding the body also has an effect on the physical body. In fact physical structures are composed of atoms and matter, which are all simply derivatives of energy. The whole of the physical body and indeed the physical world, is based on energy manifesting in different forms. So the human body can be considered to be a miniature cosmos of energy. Human energy is therefore both an *indicator* and a *regulator.* If the energy flow is poor or irregular, it will eventually start to affect the mental and physical aspects of the body in some way.

Harmony in the physical body is reflected by harmony in the energy flow and vice versa. If our physical body is unwell, this is reflected in the way our energy is liberated and flows. In this case, the energy may not flow well and may become blocked. The energy may become weak. When energy does not flow or becomes weak, an imbalance occurs.

Minor imbalances in energy rectify themselves in time. The natural flow of energy gradually disperses small, minor blocks. However, if an imbalance occurs over a sustained period, then the block is unlikely to disperse of its own accord. Once this blocked energy flow becomes established, the energy begins to affect the physical balance of the body and dysfunctional patterns start to appear in the functioning of the body, and mind. At this point afflictions of a physical, emotional or mental nature often manifest.

Now that we have considered what energy is, we shall now consider how energy is characterised, by different cultures. We shall start with the *western view*. In the west, new age ideas and therapies are currently very popular. In these cultures, people often refer to human energy in terms of the aura and the chakas.

People have found that a kind of energy envelope surrounds the physical body. This is often termed *the aura*. Furthermore, there are certain areas of this energy envelope where energy collects and can be experienced and manipulated readily. Small areas such as this, have been termed "tsubo". These are usually thought of as the acupuncture points. Larger energy areas on the energetic field are classically known as chakras.

As you read through this book you will gradually see that these ideas terms and Western ideas are really adaptations of much more established theories that have been found in eastern cultures for thousands of years. What is also apparent is that the categories and experiences that emerged in the qualitative analysis described earlier, are things that have been explained in the Taoist, Tibetan and Hindu explanations of energy for many thousands of years.

Western New Age Perspectives
The Aura and the Chakras

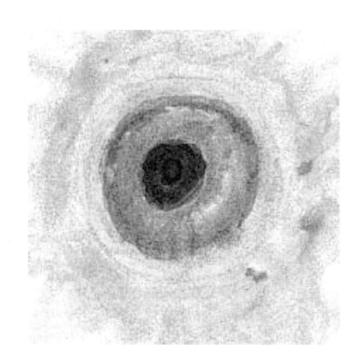

The Aura

The human aura is commonly depicted in many therapies such as the many forms of healing and also reiki. The aura is essentially the energy field that surrounds the body.

This energy field is really combination of the energy produced by the body and an element of energy from another source - part of the life energy derived from our spiritual being, whatever we want to call it. The aura or energy field is a reflection of our spiritual life, our body and our mind. Changes in our thoughts, our physical body and our emotions all have consequences for the energetic pattern that is expressed in our aura.

Some people have termed the auric field as a conscious energy or a manifestation of universal consciousness and hence the aura is considered to comprise of a spiritual aspect. The aura is considered to be quite important; it is an expression of our consciousness and it conveys not only our actions but also our unconscious self. As it contains reference to our undisclosed motives it is considered to act as an indicator of ones higher potential and spiritual development.

The aura is often depicted as existing in a number of layers (usually seven layers). These layers are sometimes called "bodies". They surround each other, a little like the layers of an onion or sprout. Each layer penetrates the other to form an integrated energy field around the physical body of a living being. The aura is densest close to the body and becomes finer moving away from it . Most human auras extend from between one and five feet outwards from the body. In more spiritually developed individuals the aura can extend outward much greater distances, up to fifty feet from the body.

As the energy field originates from the physical body itself and then extends through the other aspects of energy, such a *source*. The aura can be considered to reflect and encompass all facets of worldly life and provide an indicator of all aspects of our consciousness: our physical, mental and spiritual aspects. Each layer of aura is though to relate to a chakra. For this reason, there are seven layers of the aura, as there are seven major chakras. The chakras will be introduced later.

Gradually as the energy field extends away from the physical body, the energy builds a higher level of "vibration". For this reason, the more subtle levels are increasingly difficult to sense, and to characterise as they begin to extend into areas that are difficult to comprehend. This is why traditions such as Taoism find that there is no adequate definition of "source" as this type of energy goes beyond our comprehension.

The Seven Bodies

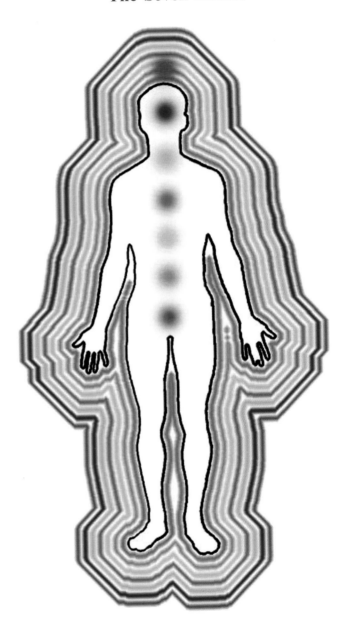

The Seven Bodies

Each layer (also termed body) of the aura interpenetrates each of the other layers. The vibration of each level becomes finer and higher as we go from the inside out. There has been considerable variation regarding the way that the aura is described, nevertheless it is commonly accepted that the human aura has seven layers or bodies. This description is by no means a "true" or absolute description. The reason for this is that the layers are not really layers but areas of different frequency that interpenetrate each other. The energy field changes constantly and is not static, and so any description of it is merely a snap shot in time of what is happening. This is the reason why the aura is perceived markedly different by different people.

What follows is a general consensus of how the aura has been depicted as seven bodies. The seven bodies that make up the aura are most popularly and commonly characterised as follows:

The etheric body, is the name that has been given to the first layer of aura. This energy envelope follows the outlines of the physical body. The etheric body is thought to integrate and support the biological and chemical processes of the physical body. The etheric body is sometimes called the lower astral body. It is sometimes perceived as being a bluish or greyish layer that extends an inch or two out from the body. It is the layer of the aura that is easiest to see. Contained in this energy vibration are vibrations concerning the physical body functions, physical sensations of pain and pleasure.

The second layer of the aura is called **the emotional body**, and as the name suggests functions to support the emotions. This energy vibration is home to the emotional aspects of our lives and being. The layer extends from about one to six inches out from the physical body.

The third layer of the aura is **the mental body** and is related to the psychological processes that occur in the person. Here the energy characterises the thought processes and conscious thinking. These three bodies are the lower astral and together are said to make up and reflect the personality.

As you can see although the second and third layers are characterised as separate they are in fact part of one another. As one moves further through the layers of the aura it becomes more difficult to separate them in terms of their attributes and functions.

The forth layer of the aura is known as **the astral body**. At this point the aura is much more diffuse and harder to visualise. The astral body is thought to extend about 30-50 cm around the physical body. The astral body acts to integrate the lower three vibrations with the higher ones.

The fifth layer of aura is known as **the etheric body** and extends about 1 metre from the physical body. This layer is called a template as it is thought to mirror the other layers that surround it. In this energy vibrations the higher aspects of the will have a stronger connection with the divine. It has been very rare for people to be aware of this layer.

The sixth layer is known as **the celestial body**

The seventh layer of aura is known as **the ketheric body**. This layer extends about two metres from the physical body surface. The 7th layer of aura is quite special in that it is record of the entire life experience of the individual. The seventh layer is also considered to be the most refined and most permanent of the energetic layers, and some say that it is the seventh layer that relates most closely to "source" energy and to previous life.

The human energy is never completely still; even when the body is resting there are thoughts and feeling being processed. Hence the aura is never static either. The aura constantly is changing shape, size and appearance, depending on a number of factors. State of health, physical and psychological activity, time of day, emotionality, all affect how the aura appears.

Some people who are clairvoyant, can see the auric field, and the aura at a given moment, can also be captured by Kirlian photography.

Imaging the Aura and Kirlian Photography

The idea that one might be able to capture the human aura on film has been a topic of much interest. Certainly many ancient and classical arts depict people with halos and auric fields, and so it is clear that people have always believed that such an energy field exists.

In the early part of the century, a doctor in London, called Walter Kilner used an ultra violet lamp as a method of viewing the aura. Kilner claimed that using this apparatus allowed him to see faint shapes and shadows around the body. He developed a theory suggesting that there was a relationship between the appearance of these shapes and a persons health. Then, in 1939 Semyon Davidovich Kirlian, developed what has become known as Kirlian photography.

Kirlian photography is a technique of imaging objects inside an electric field. The resulting photographs captured the shapes but with the added advantage of colour. This was considered to be the aura. Nevertheless, there is a dispute as to what these images are actually revealing. A number of different ideas have been postulated, with images revealing: physical energy, psychic energy, the etheric body, or simply an electric charge. The reaction from the scientific community is the same as to any paranormal phenomena.

An aura photograph taken at a recent new age exhibition in London UK. Is this a true representation of Marie's aura?

One word of caution regarding so called aura pictures such as the one illustrated above. Some, "so called" aura cameras are cameras with light emitting diodes (LEDs) inside the camera enclosure. These LEDs light according to skin resistance that is measured from the subjects skin, using a plate or sensor. The light emitted from the diodes fog the photographic film producing coloured clouds. Such pictures are obviously not the aura, but a new age gimmic. Certainly the true Kirlian technique is expensive, dangerous and not readily available. One camera manufacturer asserts that a test can be made of dubious cameras by placing the hands on the sensory plate and taking a photograph when the person is not sitting in front of the camera lens If a coloured aura appears on the resulting print in the absence of the persons body, then it is likely the camera is not based on the original Kirlian technique, but contains LEDs that simply fog the photographic film. Unless of course some friendly spook has happened to kindly sit in the hot seat for you!

In spite of this concern there are some interesting things occur when objects are photographed using appropriate techniques. Studies have shown that a plants energy field changes as a human hand approaches to pick it. Once a leaf has been picked, a glowing outline of the missing area still appears on the film. Some people use this as evidence that the imaging technique is recording the etheric body of the aura.

What information do we get from the aura?

For those of a therapy background the aura is important as it reflects the state of health. Someone who is healthy and well has a clear energy field that is free from defects. Any dysfunction, whether it be psychological, emotional, or physical will be expressed, represented and manifest in the aura. The converse is also true. Trauma or ill heath will result in an aura that is damaged or full of impure energy.

Blockages then form in the energy field. If these blockages do not disperse, dysfunctional patterns will emerge in the persons, behaviours, cognitions or physical self. The actual way that a These dysfunctional patterns manifests in the body, mind and spirit will vary from person to person. This is because each person has unique energy, but they eventually lead to problems in the worldly life.

Viewing the Aura

What might you perceive as you observe the aura and the information and colours in the aura? Generally what most people see when they observe an aura is some of the information from the first or etheric body visible next to the skin. Many people see this part of the auras as "heat waves" or moving outlines. This is often perceived as a bluish or greyish or whitish field. This field may have changes in shape where there are weak spots. Blockages or traumas may appear as thinning or swelling or breaks in the aura. On occasion the observer may also perceive information from the second or emotional body which is often seen as clouds of colour. In this layer blockages and traumas show up as muddy grey fogs, or dark areas. Sometimes shapes and symbols are seen in this energy field .

Many people claim that there is a set colour code for the aura. However, in my experience this is not the case. Each observer will experience a different perception of the same thing. This occurs as the observer can only experience the energy of someone else's aura by using their own energy. In other words what I personally perceive as blue, someone else may experience as purple. This is further complicated by the fact that each layer or body of the aura is not separate, but inter-twinned. So how might anyone learn to read the aura? The answer is that the observer must learn their own personal code and understand their own perceptions, rather than what is written in someone else's personal code. This is just the same as the categories of energy that people were experiencing when sensing energy earlier in this book. Some people sensed coolness, whereas some sensed heat or tingling. What the individuals need to learn is what this sensation means to them. For this reason I have not included a section on auric colours in this book.

So far this chapter has described the basic characteristics of the energy enveloping the body known as the aura. Energy also tends to collect in specific areas of the energetic field. These areas are a little like power stations, or votices. Such areas are described in almost every belief system and energy paradigm. These areas where energy tends to gather and collect to form vortices. These are termed the chakras.

The Chakras

In Sanskrit the word chakra means wheel. The word chakra therefore is the word used to name what has been depicted as circular energy centres that are found to surround the body. The notion of chakras has emerged from ancient India, although many of the associations that are considered in this chapter are the products of more modern ideas from new age healing, crystals, reiki etc.

The chakra's are energy centres or energy vortices. You may think of them as very large tsubo's i.e. areas where energy collects or junctions where energy meets. You will see that the nature of the chakras emerges from the way that energy flows along the central channels, which are depicted in the section of Hindu ideas of energy, which can be found later in this book.

Chakras are patterns of energy, and are shaped something like whirlpools. The chakra are considered to be junctions or areas where one can sense and manipulate energy. The system of chakras has evolved over many years, and most of the material about them has been derived and adapted from ancient India scripts.

There are a number of chakra's situated around the body. The chakras inter-penetrate and extend beyond the visible physical body. Their vortices lie around and through the body, and tend to be situated along a line running along the spinal cord. This line corresponds to the central energy channels, which will be detailed later. Each chakra occurs near to or over a major nerve plexus; an area where many nerves meet.

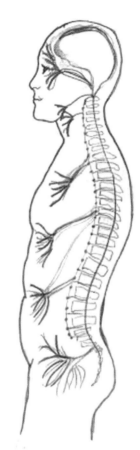

The Major Nerve Plexus

Notice that the position of the plexus corresponds to the position of the major chakras

The actual number of these chakras is a subject of debate, however classically people consider there are seven major chakra's, and upto twenty one minor ones. One may think of the major chakras as primary energy centres, with each centre having its own characteristics. Each chakra relates to a physical function and an emotion and each chakra has a color of the visible light spectrum associated with it.

It is important to note, however, that these associations, particularly those with colour, are a convenience and merely symbolic. In reality each chakra displays a number of varying colours, in the same ways as the aura changes colour.

It is also important to remember that the chakras do not actually exist as a structure in the physical body as they are energy patterns. There are certain specific locations on the body, where the chakras usually form and hence the major chakras are considered to be located and sensed in particular regions. Nevertheless, an energy votrex has the potential to occur anywhere in the energetic body depending on the flow of energy.

The seven major or "classical" chakras are located from the head to the base of the spine as follows: the base, the sacral, the solar plexus, the heart, the throat, the brow, and the crown (above the head). The chakras distribute energy to the different areas of the body. As the chakras are often located over endocrine glands they are also thought to influence endocrine function. This is one of the reasons why the chakras are considered to be a major influence in heath and well being. Later we shall discuss the location of other minor chakras.

Energy is often described as flowing from the lower chakras upwards to the higher chakras. As the energy flows in this direction, consciousness is often characterised as moving from simple, base instincts to more refined spiritual thought. I would however, disagree with this idea. This idea suggests that the lower levels are not as important. Of course all of the chakras make up the whole being - each is necessary, and certainly in terms of other theories of energy, such as yin-yang, one cannot have one without the other (one cannot have heaven without earth). In a later chapter when we discuss yin-yang theory this becomes very apparent.

Some people have also described the chakras as having a front and a rear component. However, the chakra is an energetic body and so there is no reason why the energy vortex is not a single unitary area. The reason that people have characterised that chakras as having a front and rear component, is to allow a simple explanation for those who perform hands on healing techniques. As healers work at the front and/or the back of the body, the front/back idea is a very convenient distinction. Nevertheless, as energy is limitless, and indeed, makes up the physical body, it seems quite bizarre to suggest the energy forms a distinct front and back! You should always remember that chakras are areas that appear a little like a hologram. It is therefore not necessary to consider the chakra to have front and rear area, as the vortex extends throughout the physical body rather than being separated by it.

As mentioned previously, each chakra has a number of different associations. These associations relate to thoughts, emotions, physical body structures, colours and body processes and functions.   Also included are the musical notes associated with each chakra. A seed syllable is also given. The seed syllable can be thought of as a mantra sound that has a particular affinity with the chakra and can be used to activate the area. The following is a summary of these associations.

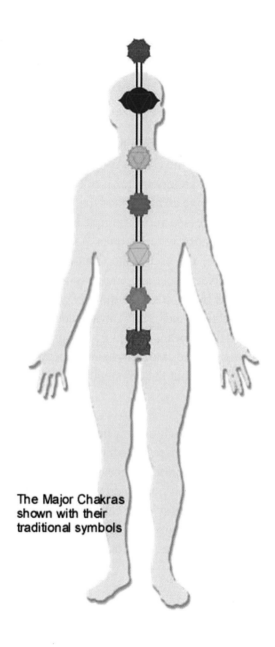

The Major Chakras shown with their traditional symbols

Chakra Associations and Correspondences

The Crown Chakra:
Key attributes of the Crown Chakra include: the colour violet, totality of being, and spiritual perfection.

The crown chakra is located above the head. It is the largest chakra and is made up of two energy vortex. It is often described as a lotus having one thousand petals of rainbow colours. The sanskrit name for this energy centre is Sahasrara. The crown centre is considered to be the seat of the soul. As with the third eye centre, the crown chakra is also is linked to the pituitary and pineal glands. It is associated with the perfection of mind, body and spirit. The role of the crown chakra is to govern one's connection with universal consciousness. It acts to produce spiritual aspirations and a search for knowledge and the truth. These spiritual aspirations are considered to produce a drive for the person to seek a oneness with everything that is. The crown chakra therefore functions as our connection with the higher self and the divine.

The colour associated with this chakra is violet, although people also say that there is a gold colour in the centre. The crown area is associated with bliss, unity and spiritual connectivity. It is one of the areas where life-force enters into the chakra system.

The crown chakra is thought to enlarge with spiritual development, and this is often depicted as a halo in symbolic pictures of various religious deities. In some deities there is a topknot or extended area on this part of the head, symbolising a highly developed spiritual connection.

The element associated with the chakra is space and light, expressing as emptiness. This is why the chakra yields a sense of peace. The physical body structures that are associated with the crown chakra are the brain and pineal gland. The crown is also associated with the ketheric body of the aura.

When the energy in this chakra is balanced, the person feels open and has total access to the unconscious, feels spiritual, peaceful, and joyful. Energetic imbalances in the crown chakra, manifest in a number of ways: Excessive energy in this area manifests as frustration, and depression. Self destructive actions may occur. In contrast, deficient energy in the crown chakra manifests as an inability to make decisions, feelings of being misunderstood and having a negative self image which is often accompanied with depression.

The sound or note associated with this chakra is "B" and the seed syllable is OM. Aromas that have an affinity with this chakra are blends of rose, jasmine, frankinscence. The crystals associated with this chakra are amethyst, fluorite and clear quartz.

The Brow Chakra (or Third Eye Chakra)
Key attributes of the brow chakra include: the colour Indigo and the ability to visualise and use psychic insight.

The brow chakra is located in the centre of the forehead between the eyes. It is associated with the colour indigo and it is considered to be the psychic centre, that enables foresight, vision. It is associated with intuition. The Sanskrit name for this chakra is Ajna and the chakra is often associated with the cellestial body.

This chakra is often given the nickname of 'the third eye', and it is linked to the pituitary and pineal glands. It is the seat of higher consciousness and spiritual powers. The brow chakra governs intuition, visions and dreams and therefore the brow chakra is the source of insight. Clairvoyance and psychic sensitivity are generated by this centre. The brow area also controls the body's eyes, nerves, head and brain. The element associated with this chakra is ether, expressing as light, and the physical body areas that are associated with this chakra are the eyes, nose, ears and pituitary gland.

When the brow chakra energy is balanced the individual projects a charismatic nature, and experiences a number of different psychic experiences and intuitions. The individual also becomes interested in developing and achieving an idealistic position in life. Imbalances in this chakra manifest as a tendency to worry. When there is an excess of energy in the brow chakra the person appears cold, proud and sometimes authoritarian, whereas if the energy in this area is deficient, the person appears to have doubts, and is hyper-sensitive.

The sound or note associated with this chakra is "A" and the seed syllable is also OM. An aromas that have an affinity with this chakra is rosemary and jasmine. The crystals associated with this chakra are lapis lazuli, sodalite, azurite, and kyanite

The Throat Chakra

Key attributes of the throat chakra include: the colour blue, the ability to communicate and to express oneself with creative expression.

The throat chakra is located at the centre of the neck. It is associated with the colour bright blue. The Sanskrit name for this chakra is Visuddha. The throat chakra is symbolic of communication, hence, it is associated with translating feelings into spoken words. It is also associated with creativity and expression. The element associated with the centre is sound. The throat chakra forms a link between emotion and thought. Its element of this chakra is a combination of fire and ether expressing as sound. Therefore, it is traditionally associated with self-expression through thoughts, writing and speech. Physically, the throat chakra is linked to the thyroid gland and has also been described as influencing the throat, ears, nose, mouth and neck.

When the throat chakra is in balance, the person appears to be contented and centred. However, if there is an excess of energy in the chakra, the person will become arrogant and self righteous and there will be a tendency to talk negatively. If there is a deficiency in the energy in the throat chakra, the person would appear timid, quiet, and weak. They would not be able to express their thoughts and feelings and their communication would appear inconsistent. There may also be a tendency to suppress feelings.

The sound or note associated with this chakra is "G" and the seed syllable is HAM. The chakra is associated with the etheric body. Chamomile has a strong affinity with this chakra. The crystals associated with this chakra are aquamarine, blue lace agate, and turquoise.

The Heart Chakra
Key attributesof the heart chakra include: the colour Green, a capacity for universal love, compassion, and empathy.

The Heart Chakra is located on the median line of the body near to the heart. The colour associated with this chakra is green. The Sanskrit name for this Chakra is Anahata. The heart is associated with astral consciousness and the element air.

This is linked to the thymus and controls the immune system. It is the seat of the 'higher or deeper' emotions such as love, compassion and honesty. The energies from this centre affect the heart, lungs, upper chest, back and bronchial tubes. It is no surprise then that the element associated with this chakra is air. The heart chakra is considered to be very important for a number of reasons. In particular, it integrates the higher and lower chakra energies. The heart centre is associated with the seat of ones own healing energy, and ones innermost desires and dreams.

In terms of the physical body, heart chakra is associated with the physical structures of the heart, lungs and the lymph glands. It is also associated with the blood pressure, and the vascular system in general.

When the heart chakra is in balance, the person is compassionate, and can see the good in others. A desire to nurture will be apparent and the person will be in touch with their own feelings. They will have empathy and present to the world as open, adaptable, and generous. If there is any imbalance in the heart chakra, the person will be cold and lack compassion and morality. They will be insecure in most aspects of their life, and be jealous, possessive and miss-trust others. An excess of energy in the heart chakra makes one critical, demanding, possessive, and there is a tendency for manic – depressive behaviour. The person may appear full of anger, and always blaming others. If energy in the heart chakra is deficient there is self pity self, and a need for constant confirmation of self worth. The main indication of this deficiency is uncertainty about the self and an inability to enforce will. There is also a feeling of being unloved.

The sound or note associated with this chakra is "F" and the seed syllable is YAM. Aromatics that have an affinity with this chakra are lavender, rose or bergamot. The crystals associated with this chakra is, malachite and green aventurine, bloodstone and amozonite.

The Solar Plexus Chakra
Key attributes of the solar plexus chakra include: the colour yellow. The dynamic creation and projection of self as an individual.

The solar plexus chakra is located at the solar plexus (just below the sternum). This is an important centre for distributing energy. The solar plexus is sometimes called the power centre or clearing centre. The solar plexus is therefore a major area for interpreting energy from the other centres. The sanskrit name for the solar plexus is Manipura and the element of the chakra is fire.

The solar plexus is linked to the digestive system, the pancreas liver, diaphragm and stomach. This centre is our psychic battery and the storehouse of our positive energy. Also it is the link between the mind and the emotions and the area we process negative feelings. The solar plexus is also associated with controlled power and its attributes: assertiveness, confidence. It is the motivating force that produces skilful means.

When the energy of the chakra is balanced, the person appears outgoing, cheerful, and respectful. A person with a balanced solar plexus is intellectual, self confident and flexible. If there is an excess of energy in the solar plexus the person will be demanding and judgmental. They will become a perfectionist and there will be a tendency for them to over work, and be a workaholic. These people will find it very difficult to relax. If there is a deficiency of energy in the solar plexus the person will be depressed, and there will be a tendency to blame others. The person will easily hurt and take offence. They may feel that they have not received the recognition that they are entitled to. They will fear anything new and may also feel isolated. The lack of confidence may also be accompanied with other psychological problems.

The sound or note associated with this chakra is "E" and the seed syllable is RAM. The aromatic that has a great affinity with this chakra is juniper .The crystals and gem stones associated with this chakra are tigers eye, amber, iron pyrites and rutilated quartz.

The Sacral Chakra (the Spleen Chakra)
Key attributes of the sacral chakra include: the colour orange and the experience of desire & attraction.

The sacral chakra is sometimes called the spleen chakra, although one should note that the spleen organ of the physical body is located in a much higher position in the abdomen. The sacral chakra is located just above the sex organs in the lower abdomen. The Sanskrit name for this chakra is Svadishana.

The sacral chakra is linked with the adrenals and the release of adrenaline into the body. Its element is water and if this centre is out of balance your 'flight or flight' response may be over active. This centre also has a cleansing function by filtering out negative influences. The spleen itself is often considered the store of psychic energy.

This chakra affects the general vitality of a person. The colour associated with this chakra is orange. The sacral chakra is associated with attraction, pleasure and satisfaction. The sacral chakra is associated with the physical structures of the kidneys, adrenals and the skin, together with the female reproductive organs.

When the sacral energy is balanced, there is a concern for others and a friendly good humoured disposition. If the energy in the sacrum becomes excessive, there will be a tendency for the person to be aggressive and manipulative. The individual will be highly strung and seek power and control. This will be accompanied with arrogance and pride. If the energy in the sacrum is deficient, the person will fell guilt and be hyper- sensitive, shy and very timid. There will be a difficulty in showing emotion and there may be social anxiety.

The sound or note associated with this chakra is "D" and the seed syllable is VAM. Aromatics that have an affinity with this chakra are rose, sandalwood and myrrh. The crystals that are good for this chakra are carnelian and citrine.

The Root Chakra (or Base Chakra)

Key attributes of the root chakra include: the colour red, basic instincts and drives, such as the need to survive and the id of personality.

The Root (also called the Base) chakra is located at the base of the spine. The colour associated with this chakra is red and the sanskrit name for the chakra is Muladhara. This chakra is of importance to *kundalini*; this area provides energy for the other chakras. The base chakra also energises, and strengthens the whole physical body.

The base chakra is associated element is Earth and it corresponds to the sense of smell, physical energy and vitality. It is the grounding or primary energy source. This area is said to have the knowledge of all creation, due to its links with reproduction. This chakra is also the chakra of base instinct and is associated with motivation. The chakra also is the seat of passion, and governs the relationship with money and material things. The base chakra is associated with the spine, the male reproductive organs and the reproductive anatomy.

When the base chakra is in balance, the person appears centred and is able to feel secure and well grounded. If the base chakra energy becomes in excess the person appears greedy, and egotistic. They will be highly strung and become overly materialistic. There may also be a tendency to be violent or dishonest. If there is a deficiency in the base chakra energy, the person would lack confidence and feel weak , powerless and sexually inadequate. There may also be feelings of frustration and a lack of grounding.

The sound or note associated with this chakra is "C" and the seed syllable is LAM. Aromatic oils that have an affinity with this chakra are the base notes and also citrus-spice blends that include, vetiver, lemon and frankincense. The crystals of gems that are good for this chakra are Hematite (for grounding) jasper, ruby and garnet.

The Minor Chakras

In addition to the seven classic chakras there are also some other chakra energy centres that are very important. There are said to be twenty one minor chakras. These minor chakras are located in various positions around the body: in front of the ears and behind the eyes, over major organs, behind the knees, and over the hands and feet. For those involved in healing perhaps the most important of these are those of the hands and feet.

The Foot Chakra

The Foot chakra is sometimes considered part of the root chakra. There is one single foot chakra, and it is located in located in the arch of each foot, half being represented in both feet. The colour associated with this chakra is red, the same as the root chakra.

The foot chakra is considered to be very important as this is where the energy makes a link with "source energy". At this point the energy either returns into the energy field or makes a connection with the earth to become grounded. This is the physical bodies grounding point where body energy is transformed into earth energy and the reverse. This connectivity is considered to be very important for health and well being, as energy that flows well through the foot chakra does not block to become negative. This has been described as a lightening strike. Once the lightening has travelled into the earth it is no longer a danger. A foot chakra that is blocked allows energy to build up casing energy in the body to become stagnant and blocked.

The Hand Chakra

This chakra is located in the palm of the hand. The hand chakra is associated with truth and psychological clarity. Some people claim that the hand chakra is integrated with the heart and throat chakra areas, allowing expression of these attributes. There are also small chakras in each finger.

Summary of the Western View: The Aura and the Chakras

The body energy is characterised as envelopes that surround the body that we call the aura. The aura often portrayed as seven layers or bodies. The innermost layer, nearest to the physical body being called the etheric body.

The chakras are energy centres that permeate the physical body and the energetic body that surrounds the human. Chakras are depicted as wheel like votices where energy collects.

There are seven major chakras that relate closely to the layers of the aura. Each chakra is thought to serve a different function and has different physical, emotional and psychological attributes.

The Laws of Yin-Yang

Yin and Yang

The concept of yin yang is central to any theory that aims to achieve balance. Although many people have heard of yin yang, few of the modern therapies apply its principles into their practice. Nevertheless, it remains a very powerful theory, and one that should not be ignored.

The concept of yin and yang emerge from Taoist philosophy and early theory of yin-yang was formed in the Yin and Zhou dynasties (16th century - 221 B.C.).

The term yin-yang first appeared in "The Book of Changes":

"Yin and yang reflect all the forms and characteristics existing in the universe".

The Taoists identified that with nature there appeared a cyclic, rhythmic pattern to life. These ideas were formulated and became what is now termed yin yang theory.

Most people will be aware of some of the basic ideas behind yin and yang. Yin and yang are the two most basic divisions into which we can characterise energy. The black and white symbol, with its swirl, is a capture the qualities of yin and yang.

Yin and Yang

It is important to remember that yin yang not only characterises the energetic qualities of human's, but that yin yang theory applies to the entire universe. Yin yang theory contains the cycle of sun, four seasons, and the yearly calendar. This is particularly apparent when one considers other aspects of oriental life, and soon it is clear that the ideas of yin & yang can be found everywhere in oriental cultures. The seasons are a classic example given to students. Spring and summer are seen as the yang times of the year, here energy is becoming most active. Spring is a time for renewal, growth and activity. In contrast, autumn and winter are times where energy is waning and slowing down, and so these periods are seen as the yin times of the year.

Another classic example is the time of day. This can also be characterised in terms of yin and yang, with daytime being most yang and night time being most yin.

Now if one considers any aspect of the universe, one could apply these ideas. So the yin yang system is really a metaphor of a dynamic system where the whole universe is constantly changing, flowing, and transforming.

We can then extend this idea to human health and balance. First, note that according to yin yang theory, all things contain a microcosm of the universe. The human being is no different. So the human entity embodies the principles of yin and yang. Man is therefore a microcosm of substance and matter that is determined by energy. Yin yang theory is therefore a very powerful tool for diagnosis, healing and for understanding the environment and the universe.

The patterns and rhythms that were noted in yin yang theory were extended and the patterns that energies were found to take were formulated into the principles (laws) or precepts of yin & yang. These precepts were: opposition, dependence, mutual consumption, and transformation

The precept of opposition

Everything in the universe has opposing aspects. Yin & yang are often considered to be mutually dependent opposites; this captures the duality of nature and its inter-dependence. Ying and yang are often presented as a table of opposites. For example, cold vs. hot (yin is cold, yang is hot) masculine vs. feminine (yin is feminine and yang is masculine). These opposites are classically described as yin being like night and yang being like day. However, the most fundamental thing to note about yin and yang is that although they may first appear as opposites, they are in fact compliments, the relationship between yin and yang is not linear, as you move through yang, you do not move further away from the yin aspect, rather your move closer to it. For a moment, consider the yin yang symbol. Notice that the colours swirl and blend into each other. There is no definite beginning or end, rather the tones blend into one another. This is very important when we consider energy in the human body. This will become more apparent as we consider yin yang law further, in particular the precept of transformation and infinite divisibility.

The precept of transformation

As you viewed the symbol, and moved around the swirling pattern you can see clearly that yin can become yang and yang can become yin. As one moves around the symbol each aspect becomes weaker and then stronger. As you move through yang you move both towards and away from yin. This is the precept of transformation, where one energetic state gradually changes into the next one.

The precept of dependence and mutual consumption

Yin & yang each depend on each of other. You cannot have yin without yang and vice versa. Thinking of the symbol, the circle would not be complete without both aspects, the black and the white. In addition, it is not better to have more black or white – i.e. it is not better to have more yin than yang etc. What is important is that there is a balance. Notice on the symbol that there is equality between the black and white. So, yin & yang define each other and therefore one cannot exist without the other. This can be observed in everything. Classically this has been described in the following way: you cannot comprehend calm without understanding what chaos is. Eventually as chaos declines calm appears. I remember having a realisation of this aspect of yin yang when, I was attending a Dorje Sempa initiatiation, given from a very high lama from Tibet. Just before performing the empowerment, the Lama explained that due to yin-yang, he would need to occupy the negative forces whilst he performed the empowerment. The deity Dorje Sempa is the embodiment of Buddha nature that cleanses us of negative karma, and as such is a very positive pure force. Rinpoche explained that due to yin-yang whenever one invites such a power into your mind, the opposing force also comes with it, and unless tackled, this could create a barrier for the good that was being done. I remember thinking what a wonderful example of yin-yang theory this was.

The precept of infinite divisibility

So far we have considered yin and yang as complimentary forces, but actually we can now go one step further and state that yin and yang can be found within each other. Anything energetic can be subdivided again and again. A good example of this would be the human body. It is easy for us to think of ourselves as a single unit. However, we could then think of ourselves as many different cells. On closer examination each cell has organelles within it. Each of those organelles has a different function, just as our body organs serve to have different functions for our bodies. If we examine one single organelle we find within it there are a number of different processes going on. Take for example the nucleus of a cell. Inside the nucleus is the genetic material and chromosomes that have the ability to replicate. You may consider the replication process as quite active. It happens all the time and is the basis of how the cells regenerate. The process of regeneration (or transcription and translation as it is known) involves both active and passive phases. Indeed, the micro-structures of the nucleus also have areas that have both active and passive qualities. So, what we first thought of as quite active, actually has passive elements within it as well. The duality of yin-yang can be seen clearly when we consider the elements or phases. Each phase has both a yin and a yang aspect which has been derived from both yin and yang.

As we have stated earlier, the concept of yin yang emerged from Taoist philosophy, nevertheless the principles of balance, and yin yang can be found in all healing systems that view the human body as a micro system of energy. For this reason, yin yang theory is particularly important.

In health and diagnosis, a condition may be classified as Yin or yang in nature. Given the way that these qualities are interdependent and cycle, any excess or deficiency will undoubtedly have an impact on the well being of the body. There are numerous permutations of Yin & Yang, and these are perhaps best characterised in Traditional Chinese Medicine (TCM). It is important to remember that both yin and yang are always present. Their dynamic interaction is the basis for diagnosing and treating any disharmony.

Human Energy   by   Dr Jarrod Hollis

The Elements

Element Theory

Element theory is a way of viewing a whole organism and trying to determine how the different parts of the organism relate to the whole. Elements break down yin and yang into symbolic descriptions that are designed to understand the different qualities that energy can express. It is important to remember that although elements may be given a label of something that is familiar to us (e.g. metal), this is not necessarily the same concept as that which we find in physical life. Instead, the label for each element is used as a metaphor for the qualities that we associate with that physical concept.

All of the element theories of energy can be seen to compliment and co-exist with the yin-yang ideas. Each of the elements is formed by a different combination, interaction or tension between yin and yang. The result is a number of elements each of which having its own particular characteristics or qualities.

Four classical elements were proposed by early philosophers and were characterised in a number of different ways. Plato considered the elements as atoms of different geometric shapes. Aristotle viewed the elements more in terms of what we think of as yin-yang: mutually dependent opposites. This idea carried through into the Middle Ages, where the elements were termed "humors" by Hippocrates. At the same time Eastern cultures were developing their own element theories and systems. I think it would be fair to say that the elements of traditional Chinese, Verdic and Tibetan medicine were all far more detailed and refined than those of the West and are still in use today.

Culturally, various different cultures have divided up and named the elements in different ways. For example, the traditional Chinese (Taoist) system describes five elements (Wood, Fire, Earth, Metal, Water). In contrast, ancient Indian ideas (Ayuvedic) portray three groupings of the elements which are formed from the basic five elements of Air, Fire, Water, Earth and Ether/Space. In Greece, five elements were considered: Earth, Water, Fire, Air and Ether. According to Tibetan culture the elements are Earth, Water, Fire, Air and Space. Nevertheless, for our purposes we need not dwell on these differences. The aim of this section is to provide some background and suggest some applications for element theory. The most well known of element theory has been derived from Taoist philosophy and so the discussion will commence with these five elements.

Taoist Five Elements (aka Five Phases or Correspondences)
The theory of the five elements was first formed in China at about the time of the Yin and Zhou dynasties (16th century - 221 B.C.). The theory of the five phases came about at about the same time as the yin yang theories. According to Taoist philosophy there are five elements. As in yin yang theory, the theory of the five phases (elements) claims that all phenomena in the universe correspond to the elements and that these are in a state of constant motion and change. The use of the word element is a little misleading and it has been suggested that this can be considered a miss-translation. It is considered more appropriate to consider transitional phases rather than elements. The elements of Fire, Earth, Water, Metal and Wood reveal to us the natural universe as we see it and know it. These same five elements are also the essential elements that in combination make us what we are - human.

Each human being, indeed everything in this universe, has its own unique nature which results from its individual yin and yang tensions; this generates the individual character or essence of being.

The elements or phases themselves can be considered as divisions of both yin and yang. Recall that in yin-yang theory one has a law of infinite divisibility, where yin and yang can be found within each other, and can be subdivided again and again. In this case, each element can be considered to be a division of both yin and yang.

In Taoist philosophy, and in Traditional Chinese Medicine, there are five elements or phases and there are Wood, Fire, Earth, Metal, Water. Each element has its own character and all of the elements have associations. The elements interact and flow in two cycles. These cycles capture the relationship and interdependence between the elements, with these cycles, making up the whole universe and the whole being.

Each element has a number of associations to the body, in terms of organs, functions, processes, emotions, thoughts and feelings. There are also associations other phenomena related to health, such as foods, materials etc. In the human body each anatomical organ and structure is related to a particular element. In this way element theory integrates the mind and body, viewing the mind and body as an interconnected whole. As the elements are inter-related they all create and restrict one another to create balance. So the important things to know about the elements are the associations with each of the elements and also ways cycles of creation and control.

There are two main cycles of interest. One is a forming cycle (shen cycle) and the other is the controlling cycle (Ko cycle). Both cycles are necessary for well being, balance and health.

The Shen Cycle
The Shen cycle is sometimes called the nourishing or forming cycle. Each element creates the next element. This cycle is often described as a mother….i.e. each element is mother to the next element in the cycle.

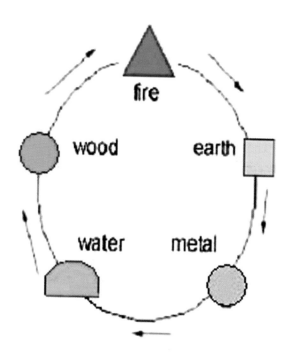

The Shen Cycle

The five elements are arranged in the circle in a particular order. According to the theory, Wood creates Fire, Fire creates Earth, Earth creates Metal, Metal creates Water and Water creates Wood. This cycle forms the elements and their associated energies are produced. For example, Water nourishes Wood, Wood fuels Fire, Fire makes ashes (Earth) Earth yields Metal (in this classical example, think of mining), Metal produces Water (in this classical example, think of condensation).

To visualise this cycle one can also think of the seasons of the year. This is another classical way of thinking about the Shen cycle. In spring energy starts to become active. Seeds germinate and plants start to grow. The sun appears to become stronger and the nights are lighter. People appear to have more energy. The pace of life quickens. Everything appears fresh. The energy is active and expanding, moving upwards as the plants grow and reach for the sky. This is the wood element.

The energy increases and gradually reaches a maximum. The season is now in the heat of summer. There is much activity. This is the fire element. Gradually all of the summer heat is used up and then towards the end of summer the evenings cool and the pace of life starts to slow. This is the end of summer and the earth element.

As the energy starts to dissipate, autumn arrives. This is the time when the leaves fall from the trees and the cooler weather moves in. Evenings start to become cooler and darker. The pace of life starts to slow. This the element of Metal where the energy appears to contract. Finally the winter arrives and the pace of life and the natural cycles are at their slowest. It is like a resting period before a new dawn. This is the water element.

In the example of the seasons you can see that the cycle of energy goes from a resting state, to a period of activity. The peak of activity then follows with a slow decline back into more a resting state. We can think of this cycle in terms of Yin-yang. The wood energy is considered to be *new yang* in character. The fire energy represents *full yang*, where energy is at its peak, The earth element is part of the cycle where there is a *balance of both yin & yang*. The metal element is a period of *new yin*, and finally the water element is a time of *full yin*. We can apply this cycle to many (if not every) aspect of life: cycles of the day and night, the seasons, the tides, and even the activity in a single cell.

The Ko Cycle (or controlling & regulating cycle)

There is also a controlling cycle that helps to keep the elements in balance. The clockwise sequence within the pentagon (see diagram below) represents the Ko cycle and is called the regulating cycle. In this cycle, one element is depicted as restraining and controlling the other elements, in an attempt to maintain balance. If nothing were stopping elements from forming, one particular element may become dominant.

The Ko cycle characterises the control, that takes place between the elements. For example, Water extinguishes Fire, Fire melts Metal, Metal cuts and Wood (an axe can cut down a tree), Wood can contain Earth (tree roots penetrate the ground and break it up), Earth absorbs Water.

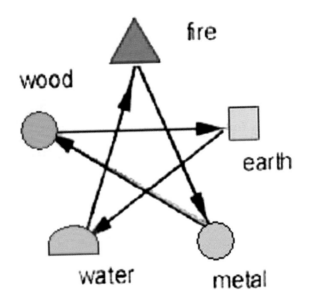

The Ko Cycle

Both the shen and the ko cycles are both necessary for the cycle to continue and for balance and harmony to occur. If the shen cycle is deficient, elements will be deficient. Similarly, if one element becomes too dominant inbalance will also occur. Ohashi gives a nice example of the necessity of the shen and ko cycles. Ohashi states:

> " *Water that flows in a river has power because of two factors: the quality of the water that nourishes the river (this corresponds to the nourishing cycle of the Five elements or five transformations), and the presence of strong banks, which provide limits to the water and thus give it direction, power and speed. If the banks give way, or if the river crests its banks, the water no longer has the same power or orderliness. It simply floods an area or sits, until it eventually receded. Movement sharply declines and then stops, until evaporation or gravity causes the water to go in other directions. As long as limits are imposed on the water, it has tremendous power...*"

Ohashi, Reading the Body: Ohashi's Book of Oriental Diagnosis

Together, the Shen and Ko cycles explain how one element can enhance or subdue another. This reaffirms that there is an inter-dependence of one element or energetic quality with another. In terms of health the controlling cycle is as important as the creative cycle. The controlling cycle is important to make sure that each element or energy type is maintained within its required limits. If one energy becomes dominant, another must become more passive than usual. At this point, disharmony starts to appear, and well being would be diminished.

In Traditional Chinese Medicine, each of the major organ systems is assigned an element. Wood is the element of the liver, fire is the element of the heart, earth is the element of the spleen, metal is the element of the lungs, and water is the element of the kidneys.

Traditional Chinese Medicine would use the Shen and Ko cycles for diagnosis and treatment. For example, following these principals you could consider a condition that was thought to exist from a wood element disharmony. One might then consider an important factor was the effect that the water element has on it. Remember that in terms of TCM, water promotes wood. Therefore in this system, if there was a wood disharmony, one possible treatment would be to treat the water element.

Another example would be imbalances in the fire and wood elements. Remember, that according to the shen cycle wood promotes fire. If the wood is in excess and too much wood is put on the fire, then the fire flares. So, to find the root of a fire disharmony, one may look to the wood element.

In terms of identifying and treating disharmonies, it can be useful to think of the elements and the shen and ko cycles in terms of the mother that gives rise to a particular element and the friend that supports a particular element. In other words, the mother and ally elements support, nurture, and strengthen a particular element, whereas the opponent element control and suppress. In reality most imbalances are best treated by strengthening the weak elements rather than trying to control and restrict an element that is in excess. This is because restricting an element will only have a limited effect, the elements will gradually return to their cycle, and the imbalance will remain. If one strengthens and corrects a weakness, all of the elements will return to their normal balanced cycle.

The relationships between the elements can be depicted in table form, as mother, ally, opponent etc.

Mother represents a nurturing quality, where one element reinforces and develops into the other. In contrast an ally represents a more general compatibility. An opponent is a relationship that dominates and attempts to destroy; where the elements are in conflict and oppose one another.

Relationships between the elements according to the Shen and Ko Cycles

	MOTHER	PROGENY	OPPONENT	ALLY
WOOD	water	fire	metal	earth
FIRE	wood	earth	water	metal
EARTH	fire	metal	wood	water
METAL	earth	water	fire	wood
WATER	metal	wood	earth	fire

In TCM diagnosis these relationships are very important, but finding the root of the problem can be difficult! Some imbalances are more common than others-for example the relationship between fire and water is important for water balance. Kidney water cools heart and heart fire warms kidney water. This is one of the ways that TCM consider balance is maintained in the body. There is also a considerable relationship between the wood element and the Earth element. Disharmonies between these two elements are some of the most common energetic patterns found in dis-ease.

Five elements theory extends to every aspect of Traditional Chinese Medicine. Besides the body's organs, tastes, smells, bodily fluids, as well as seasons, foods, directions, in fact virtually everything is assigned an element.

Of particular interest in clinical practice is the assignment of emotions. In five elements theory, each of the cardinal emotions is assigned an element. As you will see when we consider TCM, the emotions are linked to the five major organs and the meridians. According to TCM theory, emotions can be the primary causes of disease, and the assessment of emotions can be a great aid to diagnosis. For example, if a patient expresses anger excessively or inappropriately, then there is likely to be an imbalance in the wood element and with the liver organ function and meridian. If a patient develops irrational fears for example, phobias, then there is likely to be a kidney deficiency. The elements are therefore very useful in the diagnosis of disharmony.

Associations with the Elements
As we have mentioned previously each element has a number of associations and correspondences with the body, mind and nature. In terms of Traditional Chinese Medicine, each element has an association with a body organ, a sensory percept, and with the meridians or energy

channels through which our vital energy or chi flows. Each element can also be attributed to a personality type.

Wood

The wood element is associated with spring and with the emotion anger. People who have a predominantly wood constitution are described as people who like a high degree of organisation and plan well, and feel they enjoy planning, decisions, and action. They like clear well defined goals, and the future and their ability to see it can be their strength. When the wood energy is balanced, a wood person likes to plan, but also has flexibility. When out of balance they may procrastinate, and loose their focus which leads them to a sense of no hope. Alternatively they may become fixed on an inappropriate or hopeless goal. They may become over controlling. Stress, over indulging in alcohol or rich and fatty foods, or repressing strong emotions can all result in the wood element becoming out of balance.

Fire

The fire element is associated with the season summer and with the emotion of joy. People who have a predominantly fire constitution are described as people who love to reach out and be in relationship with all people. The fire personality enjoys to laugh and be outward going. The fire element is also related to ones mind and spirit. When the fire element is in balance, the person is at peace with themselves and the world. The person is mentally balanced and is able to sense a feeling of joy and space. If the fire energy becomes out of balance, the person can suffer mental unrest, anxiety and stress related disorders. People with this imbalance may also forget and invade peoples personal space. Sometimes outward expression of joy can mean that they carry a lack of joy deeper within. The fire energy can be unbalanced when there are communication problems or emotional trauma.

Earth

The earth element is associated with late summer and with the emotion of sympathy. It relates to how people look after themselves and how they nurture others around them. People who have a predominantly earth constitution have the ability to nourish and care, with mothering qualities. Food and understanding are important for those with an earth constitution. Sometimes a person of earth element can feel a sense of emptiness or neediness in their own life, and may be so fixed on caring for others, that they forget to care for themselves. When the earth element is in balance, the earth energy allows one to be empowered rather than be dependent. The foods associated with earth energy are wholemeal bread, fresh vegetables, and brown rice and pulses. Some foods tend to create imbalance in the earth energy and the earth energy is affected by poor eating habits. Foods that tend to imbalance the earth energy are dairy products and yeast.

Metal

The metal element is associated with autumn and with the emotion of grief. People who have a predominantly metal constitution tend to search for what is pure and spiritual. The metal element relates strongly with the self image, and the self concept. It relates to boarders and boundaries between the self and the outside world. People of the metal element set very high standards for themselves and others, and for the person of the metal element respect is important. When the metal energy is in balance, the person has a clear skin, and a good respiratory system. They cope with letting go, and have clarity of thought. There may at times, be a tendency to reminisce a sense of what could have been. Fresh fruit and vegetables are foods that support the metal element.

Water

The water element is associated with winter and the emotion fear. People who have a predominantly water constitution tend to have a persistence and determination. This allows them to succeed in situations that other people find too scary. A person with a balanced water element has a strong constitution and has plenty of energy. The water fosters realistic goals and healthy relationships. The water element relates strongly to balance. If the water element is out of balance, the person may sometimes feel that they harbour a sense of being frozen or overcome by their own inner fears. The water element is an energy that we inherit from our parents, and this element can be damaged with overwork, extreme cold, or emotional traumas.

The associations and correspondences for the elements are summarised in the following table. You should note that these are just a few of the very many associations for each element, and for more detail one should consult a specialist book on the topic.

Table of Associations/Correspondences with the Five Elements

	WOOD	FIRE	EARTH	METAL	WATER
Colour	Green	Red	Yellow	White	Blue/Black
Seasons	Spring	Summer	Late Summer	Autumn	Winter
Climate	Wind	Heat	Dampness	Dryness	Cold
Taste	Sour	Bitter	Sweet	Pungent	Salty
Yin Organ & Meridian	Liver	Heart	Spleen	Lungs	Kidneys
Yang Organ & Meridian	Gall Bladder	Small Intestine	Stomach	Large Intestine	Bladder
Sense Organ	Eyes	Tongue	Mouth	Nose	Ears
Body Part	Ligaments & Tendons	Blood & Blood vessels	Connective Tissue	Skin	Bones
Emotion	Anger	Joy	Worry	Grief	Fear
Voice	Shouting	Laughing	Singing	Crying	Groaning

Human Energy   by   Dr Jarrod Hollis

Elements from other Cultural Systems: India and Tibet

So far we have focussed on the five elements from Taoist philosophy that are used in the TCM approach. There are of course many other cultures that have an approach based on elements. Perhaps two of the most influential ones must be Tibetan elements and the Indian elements.

The Indian Elements: Panchbhoutika

Ayurveda has always believed that the human body is a direct replica of the Universe. The system of ayurveda comes from ancient Hindu scriptures known as the Veda. Everything in the Universe that is physical is Panchbhoutika (Pancha means five, Mahabhoota means basic elements) i.e., everything in the universe is made up of five basic elements. These five basic elements are:

Vayu (air), Teja (fire), Jala (water), Prithvi (earth), Akaasha (ether/space),

According to ayurveda every living and non living being in this universe is a combination of these five basic eternal elements. It is said that the due to is due to Prithvi (earth element) the body has a mass; due to Akaasha (ether/space element) the body structures have space; due to due to Teja (fire element) the body has colour and can digest.

Each of the elements has certain associations. For example, each element or Mahabhoota is associated with a sense.

Vata	-	Touch
Tej	-	Seeing
Jala	-	Taste
Prithvi	-	Smell
Akaasha	-	Hearing

Notice that the Indian element system is similar to the Chinese ones described previously, except that: the wood and metal elements are replaced with the elements air and ether/space. The associations with the elements are not necessarily the same.

Ether/Space is an interesting element and concept. Space acts as a place where the other elements come together and integrate. Nothing can exist without sufficient space. In classical Indian texts the element is known as ether, but in the Tibetan systems described later in this chapter, the element is called space.

The elements combine in certain ways to form and present three basic types of energy that are within everything. These are known as the doshas: *Vata, Pitta* and *Kapha.* Vata is the energy of movement, Pitta the energy of metabolism and Kapha the energy of structure.

Vata	=	Ether + Air
Pitta	=	Fire + Water
Kapha	=	Water + Earth

All beings have each of the three types: vata, pitta and kapha, but in varying proportions, with one of the types being dominant. This dominance forms a persons' constitution and is termed a dosha. I have deliberately used the term *beings* rather than *humans* as these basic types or patterns of energy are thought to be present in all creation.

When these elements are balanced, one is healthy. Illness is defined as an imbalance of these elements; all disorders are excesses of one or more element. There is also a tendency for the dosha to dominate to the extent that it becomes in excess.

For example, the vata dosha is predominantly of the element air, and so a vata type dosha tends to be thin and bony. Physical symptoms of excess air are *dehydration* and include dry skin, cracking bones, gas and constipation. Mental symptoms of excess air are *flight* and include fear, worry, anxiety and nervousness. When the air constitution (Vata dosha) is balanced people are creative, adaptable and have no physical health concerns.

People of a Pitta dosha have a constitution that is predominantly of the Fire element. In balance, these people make good leaders and are goal oriented. However, if the Pitta dosha becomes imbalanced, symptoms of *heat* manifest. Mentally people become hot tempered and irritable and physically they may develop rashes, or ulcers.

People of a Kapha dosha have a water constitution. In a balanced condition they are strong, muscular, calm. When water becomes in excess, they lack strength and substance. They develop lethargy, and physically they develop congestion, and oedema.

The doshas

There are many different associations of the doshas. As each basic type can also combine with another, it can be quite difficult to determine which type a person belongs to. However, there are a few key features that can help one identify which is a persons main mind-body constitution. There are also some features that can identify which of the doshas may be out of balance. The features can be considered as key words:

Vata:

Dry:	It resembles dryness of skin and dull hair
Quick:	Quick , fast, restless, impulsive
Cold:	Cold increases Vata,
Light:	Fasting for several days increase Vata (i.e. the body becomes lighter).

Pitta :

Hot:	Inflammation, fever, flushed skin, anger.
Sharp:	Sharp body and mind, speech
Moist:	Sweating and moist skin
Sour:	Bad breath, body odor

Kapha:

Heavy:	Heaviness is associated with Kapha.
Sweet:	Sweet things increase Kapha
Soft:	Kapha manifests as softness such as soft skin.
Slow:	Sluggishness in work, slow but steady

Each dosha can be divided again into sub-types depending on its location and function. It is not necessary for our purposes to go into these divisions. However, those who are interested may like to consult one of the many excellent books that are available on the subject.

Ayurveda treatment consists of a number of practices to balance the doshas and elements. A person experiences the elements via the senses, and so any ayurvedic treatment routine is based around the senses. The treatments include: Herbs and nutrition, massage, aromatherapy, exercise, yoga, meditation. A persons environment is also very important, and an analysis of a persons surrounds in terms of the elements helps to integrate and balance the persons energy with that of the surroundings.

Spiritual aspects of human energy in Ayuveda

The Indian traditions have quite a distinct concept of the spiritual aspects of energy. Unlike the TCM system which has many different aspects of the mind and consciousness, the Indian system has *chaitanya* which is the consciousness or spirit/soul. According to these ideas, everything in nature originates from a real of pure consciousness. This energy expands into awareness, and then creates the potential to manifest as matter, space and time. For people from a western background this concept may seem rather awesome and beyond comprehension.

Tibetan Health System and the Elements

Tibetan medicine is an assimilation of the medical traditions from Persia, China, Nepal and India. The medical system as we know it today, dates back to at least the 7th century. The historical Buddha, is said to have first taught a healing system in India during the 6th century BC and by the 7th century, a whole system of health had been established. Knowledge for the healing system being assimilated from a number of different sources, was adapted and enhanced into a complex and comprehensive system of therapy. Tibetans see health as indicative of the true nature of the human condition, and this is ultimately bound with mental, social and spiritual aspects of the person.

According to Tibetan tradition the elements can be described in terms of medicine, astrology and tantra. The Tibetan system is certainly one of the most holistic health systems in the world. It takes account of spiritual, and physical aspects of the person and aims to balance the physical, mental, spiritual and natural aspects of the person, using elements. The unity of the cosmos is depicted as a mandala known as the cosmic turtle, and this is found in systems of health and astrology.

Tibetans have a number of different health practices. Tibetan medicine itself is a system based on elements and takes into account the whole person: physical, emotional and spiritual aspects, as well as karmic influences using astrology. Therapy is carried out in many different ways; using acupuncture, diet, changes to lifestyle, spiritual practice and medicines made from minerals, herbs and precious stones.

In addition to this medicine system, is the practice of the Medicine Buddha Sadhana. The Medicine Buddha is a wonderful blue Buddha formed of Lapis Lazuli.

The Medicine Buddha Sadhana is a ritualistic practice that is found in Vajrayana Buddhism. Thrangu Rinpoche has written a wonderful book about this practice. He explains that through this practice the innate healing abilities within each of us can be accessed. Rinpoche explains that the practice is a combination of vajrayana and sutra. The practice is essentially a meditation with visualisation. It benefits the all sentient beings, including the practitioner. It therefore acts as a self healing routine, and at the same time helps others. It can be used in the same way as absent healing, or with the laying on of hands as in spiritual healing. Rinpoche explains that some people visualise a small Medicine Buddha in the location where healing is needed. Traditionally, images of the Medicine Buddha are found in medical practices. The special mantras of the Medicine Buddha are chanted when Tibetan medicines are being blended and manufactured.

Generally in the Tibetan tradition, all aspects of the cosmos are based on the same five elements of the Indian approach; space, air, fire, water, and earth. These five elements all have properties that are connected with the ones we attribute to the physical world. For example, the element Earth, is characterised as heavy, compact, and dry.

The characteristics of the elements also give rise to their function. For example the earth element gives rise to solidity, weight and mass. The water element gives rise to fluidity and cohesion (the power of the water is to keep things together), The air or wind gives rise to movement, and the fire element gives rise to temperature. Space is an interesting concept for an element. Space is the area or place where other elements interact and transform.

All organisms are comprised of these five elements, and the energetic properties manifest into matter by the three subtle principles: rlung, mkhrispa and badkan.

In the Tibetan system of medicine, the elements are referred to as humours. Akong Rinpoche, a notable Tibetan Tulku and doctor of Tibetan Medicine states that it is better to think of these as dynamics. In other words, wind dynamic refers to the element air, bile dynamic to the element fire, and phlegm dynamic to the elements of earth and water. These principles and their distribution within the person, go together to determine the personal characteristics and disposition. They are very closely linked to the principles found in Ayuveda, the doshas: vatta, pitta and kapha. They are very nicely characterised by Dr Akong Tulku Rinpoche, as a kinetic, thermal, and solid-fluid dynamic.

Rlung (similar to vatta) is a kinetic dynamic, concerned with movement and flow. For this reason it is involved with respiration, circulation in the vascular system, conduction of nervous information and excretion.

As rlung is predominately of the air element, it is rough, light, cold, subtle, and mobile.

Mkhrispa (similar to pitta) is a thermal dynamic concerned with temperature and nourishment, in terms of both the body and the mind.. Mkhrispa gives controls functions such as metabolism, liver function and vision. It enables ones mind to function with intellect. As this dynamic is mainly from the fire element, it has the qualities of fire. It is sharp, hot, and light. It is responsible for and promotes body heat.

Badkan (similar to kapha) is a solid-fluid dynamic concerned with fluids and also the support and frame of the body. It is characterised as cool, heavy, blunt, and firm.

When the principles are in balance (in Sanskrit: dhatu) there is well being. However if one of the principles is in excess or deficiency there is imbalance (Sanskrit: dosha, Tibetan nyespa).

According to the Tibetan health system, imbalances and illnesses arise from the three mental poisons; attachment, hatred and ignorance These are all closely related to the Tibetan elements: Attachment corresponds to the air element (wind humour) hatred to fire element (bile humour) and ignorance to the earth and water elements (phlegm humour).

One of the most interesting aspects about the Tibetan system of health is the way that consciousness is accounted for in precise detail. The consciousness is integrated and held in the body by the five elements. At the point of death, the elements start to dissolve and when this occurs, the consciousness is freed from the physical body.

In the Tibetan culture there are eight consciousnesses: five connected with the five senses, and three others, which include the mind and alaya, which is a kind of base or store of consciousness. One of the forces associated with the consciousness is the La, which can be loosely described as spirit. This resides in the body, and occupies a different position according to the monthly cycle. The La is similar to the Chinese concept of the Hun. There are two other energetic forces the Lü and the Sok which are more physical forces attributed to the physical body.

The Tibetan systems are based on elements, and also use the nadis from Indian and some meridians from Chinese medicine. Of particular importance is the central nadi. In Tibetan, this central path is termed the avadhuti, dhuti or royal pathway. It is along this path, that the elements dissolve at the point of death.

Traditional Chinese Medicine
The Meridians

Traditional Chinese Medicine   TCM

TCM (along with Indian and Tibetan Medicine) is one of the oldest and most established systems of health known to man. The basic principles of TCM are founded from the yin-yang and the five Taoist elements.   Before we consider how TCM views the organs and meridians of the body we should first consider how TCM views the body energy.

According to TCM there are three vital substances also known as the three treasures: Qi, Jing, and Shen.

The Three Treasures: Qi, Jing and Shen.

As I am sure you are aware, in the East, body energy is termed qi. The different forms of this word, and you will see Qi, Chi, and Ki. The energetic component of the human body is primarily composed of Qi or Chi. According to the ancient Chinese, Qi was the fundamental substance constituting the universe. The word "Qi" in traditional Chinese medicine denotes both the essential substances of the human body which maintain its vital activities, and the functional activities of the organs and tissues. According to TCM, Qi is a power or force which unifies, bonds and animates. It is described as bonding as holds particles together to materialise form (matter). Qi animates life and gives a being movement.

In the west be have a habit of using the term Chi to describe everything….Chi has become a very trendy term. Actually, to describe Qi or Chi simply as "energy" is a bit of an understatement, as there are in fact, many different sub types or classifications of Qi.

Classifications of Qi

Qi is classified into different kinds, according to its source, function and distribution. One of the basic divisions of Qi concerns where it originated, Qi can be considered to be congenital qi and/or acquired qi. Yuanqi, is the congenital Qi, which is inherited from the parents. Yongqi, yingqi and weiqi are acquired forms of Qi, derived from food. Both of these basic types of Qi are reliant on each other. Congential Qi, promotes body activity and so is involved in the liberation of the acquired Qi, and in turn, the acquired Qi fuels the body processes with nourish the congenital Qi. The term Qi is sometimes used to characterise the function or activity of the organs or meridians . In these cases it is referred to as Qi from that organ i.e. heart Qi.

Qi, has a number of different functions. It promotes growth and development, and maintains the body temperature. It acts also as a defence against pathogens and helps control and regulate the body processes.

According to TCM, there is a very particular relationship between three vital essences: Qi, body fluids and blood. Qi is involved in the transformation of these substances, and each functions to supplement and complement one another.

The Qi that flows in the meridians is referred to as zhengqi or zhenqi (vital qi). It is a combination of the qi of food essence, qingqi inhaled by the lungs, and essential qi stored in the kidney.

Jing

Jing is a little difficult to conceptualise. Jing is the essence that gives a being the potential to grow and develop. In other words, Jing is the basic life essence that allows growth, and undergo changes from birth to death.

Shen

The more spiritual aspects and the energetic aspects of consciousness that were identified at the start of this book are not actually classed as Qi. Instead, these aspects are characterised separately as; shen, po and hun. These aspects reside in various organs. For this reason they are associated with the elements. Collectively, the spiritual aspect of the human is termed shen.

The shen is the aspect of man that which makes a human more than an object in motion. In other words, the shen is consciousness or mind, and resides in the heart.

In TCM, the spirit is characterised in two ways, as an ethereal soul and a corporeal soul. The ethereal soul, is termed the hun. This can only be best described as what we think of in the West as out spirit. The hun resides in the liver. The corporeal soul is known as the po. This is another spiritual aspect that is the soul of the physical body. It resides in the lungs

There are two more aspects that are characterised by TCM. These are the yi and the zhi. The yi is best described as intellect and this resides in the spleen. The zhi is best described as will or willpower, and this resides in the kidneys. Note that according to TCM the mind is not a unitary single aspect. Instead, it comprises of many different aspects that are distributed throughout the body.

Zangfu: Yin-Yang and Organs of the Body

As we have discussed earlier the five elements have many associations and in TCM each element is associated the organs of the physical body. Each element is associated with a pair of organs: one that corresponds to the element and its yin properties, and the other which corresponds to the element and its yang properties. Therefore, the body organs have a restraining and reinforcing effect on one another as predicted by the shen and ko cycle. These pairings also relate directly to the meridians or energy channels where the vital energy or chi flows.

When the human body organs are characterised in TCM it is important to remember that in this theoretical system, the organs are not simply matter, but they carry with them a host of attributes including an emotion and a particular function. For this reason the organs are often characterised as a personality; the emperor, the minister, the general etc.

From each organ emerges an energy channel termed a meridian. The meridians have a particular route, they start or finish at the organ, and run deep within the body and then emerge and run closer to the surface of the body. In the meridians classed as yin, energy flows upwards, and the meridians are found on the yin aspect of the body; the soft inner surfaces. In contrast, in the meridians classified as yang, the energy flows in a downward direction, and the yang meridians are found nearer the surface of the body on the harder outer surfaces of the body.

Along the pathways where the meridians run close to the surface of the body, there are places where the energy in the meridian can be readily manipulated. These areas are known as tsubo and are commonly called the acupuncture points.

There are twelve classical meridians and the a number of other extraordinary meridians. You should also note that in TCM there are two meridians, that don't have a corresponding organ in a Western perspective (these are the triple heater and heart protector meridians).

The organs and their meridians (Zang fu)

In TCM, the organs and their corresponding meridians are referred to as Zang fu. Zang-fu is the general term for the organs of the human body, and includes the six zang organs (the heart, lung, spleen, liver, kidney and pericardium) the six fu organs (gallbladder, stomach, small intestine, large intestine, bladder and triple heater).

As we have already stated there are twelve classical meridians, and ten of these are connected to a body organ. The meridians gets their name from the organ with which it is associated. Each meridian is classed as either yin or yang. In general, the Yin meridians flow upwards and the Yang meridians flow downwards.

The yin meridians are associated with the Zang organs while yang meridians are associated with the fu organs. In TCM much more information is given to the zang (yin) organs, compared to the fu (yang) organs.

The following is a brief overview of the Zang fu and the meridians. Each of the organs and meridians will be presented in terms of its element. Note that the meridians often have both internal and external pathways. It is the more superficial (external) pathway that is used for treatment. The acupuncture points are found on these more superficial parts of the meridian. In the diagrams that accompany this section, only the main pathways used in classical treatment are illustrated.

The Twelve Major Meridians

The Metal Element

Meridians: Lungs and Large Intestine

Meridian Location: Arms

Main Symbolic Functions: Exchange and Elimination

Metal Expresses as:

☺ Positive, open, sociable, stable

☹ Depressive, worried, stubborn

The lung and large intestine are the meridian pairs of the metal element. They are found in the arms. The lungs and large intestine meridians are associated with exchange and elimination. The Lungs are portrayed as the master of Qi or the Prime Minister who manages domestic affairs. In TCM respiration is closely linked with the brain, and so state of mind is influenced by the lungs. The lungs govern respiration and move qi downwards, helping qi to disperse in the body. The lungs also govern the skin and house the Po or corporeal soul. (The corporeal soul is the earthly soul that surrounds the body, but does not continue after death of the physical body. It is like a template of the physical). The large Intestine expresses the will of the prime minister, and clears a path for qi, with its eliminating function.

Symbolically, the metal element is related to borders and boundaries, elimination and excretion. It evokes an ability to let go and express grief. Imbalances in the metal element are associated with feelings of isolation, depression and negativity.

Meridians of the Metal Element

Lung Meridian (Yin)
The meridian begins deep in the abdomen, and runs up the midline of the body to the throat, where it changes direction and travels to edge of the body where it surfaces. The lung meridian surfaces between the first and second ribs, just below the clavicle. The meridian runs down the inside of the arm and ends on the top of the thumb. There are 11 acupuncture points lying along the course of the lung meridian.

Large Intestine Meridian (Yang)
The meridian starts at the tip of the index finger. It runs up outside the arm to the shoulder and clavicle. Here the meridian divides into two. One branch flows through the body to the large intestine, and the other branch flows to the neck and face, ending at side of the nose. There are 20 acupuncture points along the meridian.

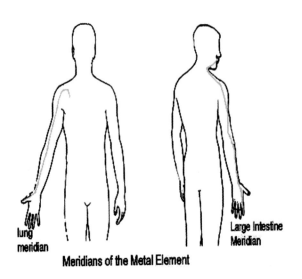

lung
meridian

Large Intestine
Meridian

Meridians of the Metal Element

The Earth Element

Meridians: Stomach and Spleen

Meridian Locations: Legs

Main Symbolic Functions: Ingestion and Digestion

Expressing as:

☺ Reliable, compassionate

☹ Cold, suspicious, cynical, over worry

The stomach and spleen are the organs and the meridians of the earth element. These organs and meridians are associated with the ingestion and digestion. In TCM the function of the spleen is vastly different from the western ideas. The stomach and spleen are likened to a worker who controls the main storehouse of food. In TCM the spleen is a very important organ as it transforms vital energies from blood and qi, food and drink, to nourish the body. The spleen governs transformation and transportation. The spleen energy moves up to nourish the brain, muscles and limbs. The spleen also regulates damp and is home to the Yi or intellect. Symbolically, the earth element is associated with nurturing, feelings of harmony with home and earth. When the earth element is out of balance, the person may feel ungrounded, and think too much, feel confused, become obsessive or worry a lot.

Meridians of the Earth Element

The Stomach Meridian (Yang)
The stomach meridian begins at the side of the nose and runs to the jaw line where it divides into two branches. One branch runs along the hairline, and another runs down along the neck and into the thorax. The meridian surfaces at the lateral side of the thigh and runs down the leg to finish at the second toe. There are 45 acupuncture points on this meridian.

The Spleen Meridian (Yin)
The spleen meridian begins at the corner of the big toe. It travels up past the front of the ankle bone and travels up the leg and thigh to the hip area where it enters the abdomen. The meridian continues through the thorax and chest and finishes a little below the armpit. There are 21 acupuncture points on the spleen meridian.

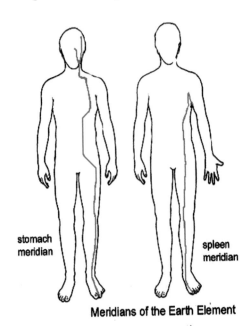

stomach meridian

spleen meridian

Meridians of the Earth Element

The Fire Element (Primary)

Meridians: Heart and Small Intestine

Meridian Location: Arms

Main Symbolic Functions: Conversion and Integration

Expressing as:

☺ Joy, calm, emotional stability

☹ Anxious, mood swings, excitable

The heart and small intestine are the organs of the primary fire element. The heart and small intestine function to convert and integrate on many levels. The heart works to integrate external stimuli with the person. The heart is depicted as the emperor or supreme commander, who governs the blood and the blood vessels and houses the Shen (mind). The heart is therefore heavily associated with awareness and communication, insight and understanding. The heart fire nurtures the development of the organs and limbs.

The small intestine acts to convert and integrate food into qi form. The small intestine also has a protective function, guarding the heart along with the heart protector.

The primary fire element is associated with compassion, joy, communication, sleep and memory. If the fire element becomes imbalanced, the person may experience a lack of compassion, be emotionally unstable, have memory problems, have a cloudy judgement, or produce an inappropriate reaction to shock.

Meridians of the Primary Fire Element

The Heart Meridian (Yin)

The heart meridian begins at the top of the heart and divides into three branches. The upper branch travels up along the neck to the eye. The lower branch goes through the diaphragm and travels to the small intestine. The middle branch travels across the chest to the armpit. It then travels down the arm to the little finger. There are nine acupuncture points on the heart meridian.

The Small Intestine Meridian (Yang)

The small intestine meridian begins at the small finger and runs through the hand and up the arm and passes near the armpit crease and onto the shoulder blades. Here the meridian travels over the neck. Here the meridian branches. One branch travels to the jaw and the face. The other branch changes direction and travels down into the body, through the chest and to the small intestine. There are 19 acupuncture points on the small intestine meridian.

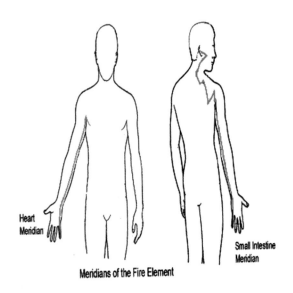

Heart
Meridian

Small Intestine
Meridian

Meridians of the Fire Element

The Fire Element (Secondary)

Meridians: Heart Protector and Triple Heater

Meridian Location: Arms

Main Symbolic Functions: Circulation and Protection

Expressing as:

☺   Joy, calm, emotional stability

☹   Anxious, mood swings, unstable

The heart protector and triple heater are the organs of the secondary fire element. There are no Western equivalent to these organs. These organs also can be found as having alternative names. The Heart protector is sometimes known as the heart governor, pericardium, heart constrictor or circulation-sex. The triple heater is sometimes called the triple warmer or triple burner. The heart protector and triple heater function to integrate and protect on many levels. The heart protector has been described as the palace official from who pleasure is derived. The heart protector conveys the intensions of the heart in terms of emotional expression. It regulates the distribution of nutrients and qi. As the name suggests the heart protector also buffers the heart from emotional trauma. The triple heater is an organ characterised as the official in charge of the pathways. Its main role is to distribute nourishing and protective qi.

The secondary fire element is associated symbolically with emotional protection and integration of all the systems. If the secondary fire element becomes out of balance, there may be a tendency to over protect, together with feelings of being emotionally vulnerable, and excessively shy. There may also be vivid dreams and/or disturbed sleep.

Meridians of the Secondary Fire Element

The Heart Protector Meridian (Yin)

The heart protector originates at the heart One branch descends into the abdomen to connect with the triple heater and the kidney. The more superficial branch travels near to the nipple on the chest and then passes up onto the arm. The meridian then travels down the arm and hand, ending at the tip of the middle finger. There are 9 acupuncture points on this meridian.

The Triple Heater Meridian (Yang)

The triple heater meridian begins at the ring finger and then travels to the wrist and up the arm to the shoulder, where it travels over the edge of the shoulder blade. Here the meridian travels up and across to the side of the neck. The path then travels along and around the back of the ear, and then finally extends onto the face, to end at the edge of the eyebrow. A further internal branch of the triple heater extends from the top of the shoulder blade and travels down into the chest and thorax. There are 23 acupuncture points on this meridian.

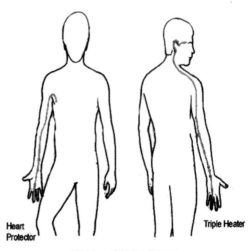

Heart
Protector

Triple Heater

Meridians of the Fire Element

The Water Element

Meridians: Kidney and Bladder

Meridian Locations: Legs and Back

Main Functions: Purification and Regulation

Expressing as:

☺   Vitality, grounded, fearless

☹   Fear, defensive, insecure, unfocused

The kidney and the bladder are the organs and meridians of the water element. Their main functions are purification and regulation. In TCM, the kidneys are very important organs. The house the zhi or will, and the jing or essence that is inherited. The kidneys are therefore the source of all yin and yang in the body. The kidneys govern birth, and reproduction, and aging. The kidneys also govern bones. One of the most important aspects of the kidneys is that they grasp the qi that enters the lungs. The kidneys also govern fluid production and function. The bladder acts to regulate and adjusts the supply-demand of the vital essences, fluids and qi.

The water element is therefore associated with purification and elimination, and symbolically with fearlessness, will power, drive and fluidity of the emotions. If the water element becomes out of balance, there may be restlessness, timidity, or phobias.

Meridians of the Water Element

The Bladder Meridian (Yang)
The bladder meridian begins at the inner corner of the eye. The meridian then runs over the head and down the back of the head, body and legs to end at the little toe. As the meridians reaches the back, it branches into two parallel routes; one branch runs near to the spine, and the other runs further apart. It is the outer branch that continues down the legs to the toe. The Bladder meridian is important as it contains points known as Yu points. These are points that correspond to organs from the other elements. There is a Yu point for every organ. There are 67 acupuncture points on the bladder meridian.

The Kidney Meridian (Yin)
The kidney meridian commences at the ball of the foot. The meridian runs to the ankle bone and then travels up the calf and onto the back of the leg. As the meridian travels up the leg to the buttock, where it goes deep into the abdomen to the kidney. After travelling internally the meridian becomes more superficial again travelling over the abdomen and the chest area, to end below the clavicle. A number of other internal meridian branches connect the kidney with the lungs, solar plexus, and heart. There are 27 acupuncture points on the kidney meridian.

Meridians of the Water Element

The Wood Element

Meridians: Liver and Gall Bladder

Meridian Location: Legs

Main Symbolic Functions: Storage and Distribution

Expressing as:

☺   gentle, quiet, flexible thinking

☹   rigid, frustrated, angry, impatient

The liver and gall bladder are the organs and meridians of the wood element. The Liver is depicted as the General in charge of planning. The liver acts to ensure that there is a smooth flow of qi throughout the body. The liver also stores and regulates blood. The liver is associates with ligaments and nerves. The liver also houses the Hun or eternal soul. The gall bladder is related with the application of ideas, that are formed in the liver.

The wood element is associated with storage, distribution and movement. Symbolically, the wood element is related to decision making, planning and execution of tasks. If the wood element becomes out of balance there may be a lack of creativity, and a tendency to overwork. This may be accompanied with impatience, excessive planning, frustration and temper tantrums.

Meridians of the Wood Element

The Gall Bladder Meridian (Yang)

The gall bladder meridian starts at the outer edge of the eye and travels down to the jaw. It then changes direction and travels to the forehead and then back to the head making a zig zag pattern around the ears and then over the head to the top of the shoulders. At this point the meridian branches. One branch descends travelling internally through the chest to reach the gall bladder. Finally the internal branch travels to the hip area. The more superficial branch travels in a zig zag fashion along the side of the body to the hip. At the hip the meridian becomes a single path and then travels along the thigh, passing down the side of the leg and ankle to end at the side of the 4th toe. There are 44 acupuncture points on the Gall Bladder meridian.

The Liver Meridian (Yin)

The liver meridian starts at the big toe and travels between the toes and up the front of the foot to a point above the ankle. The meridian then travels up the leg and thigh to the crease in the groin. Here in enters the body to travel internally to the liver. The meridian then continues up through the chest and throat to emerge at the forehead. There are 14 acupuncture points on the Liver meridian.

The following diagrams show the main paths of the twelve major meridians. For convenience on the superficial paths (where the acupuncture points are found) are shown.

112

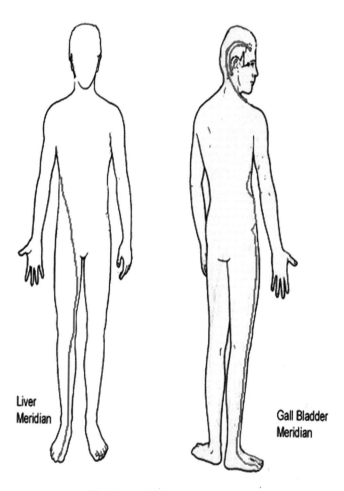

Liver
Meridian

Gall Bladder
Meridian

Meridians of the Wood Element

The Extra Ordinary Meridians

In addition to the twelve major meridians, there are eight meridians that are known as extra-ordinary meridians. They are called extra-ordinary as they do not pertain to any zangfu organs and they are not necessarily arranged in pairs. The eight extra ordianary meridians are; the governing vessel (du mai) and the conception vessel (ren mai) together with the chong, the dai, the yinwei, the yangwei, the yinqiao and the yangqiao.

In general and very simple terms, the eight extra meridians are distributed along the 12 main meridians. The extra ordinary meridians function to regulate the blood and qi of the 12 main meridians. The extra ordinary meridians extract excess qi and blood from the main meridians and store it until it is required.

Perhaps the most important extra-ordinary meridians are the conception vessel and the governing vessel.

The Conception Vessel – Ren Mai

This meridian is known as the sea of all yin as it dominates the yin of the whole body. The three yin meridians of the hand/arm and the three yin meridians of the foot/leg all join at ren mai. The meridian is also called the conception vessel as it originates in the uterus. The conception vessel functions to regulate the circulation of blood and qi in the yin meridians. It regulates the qi circulation of the chest, promotes the function of spleen and stomach and generally strengthens the body.

The Governing Vessel – Du Mai

This meridian is known as the sea of yang, as it dominates and nourishes the yang of the whole body The three yang meridians of both foot/leg and hand/arm converge into the du mai meridian. The governing vessel functions to regulate the brain, spine, urinary systems. The governing vessel also binds together all of the other meridians in the body.

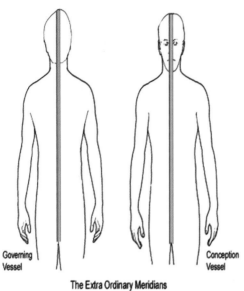

Governing
Vessel

Conception
Vessel

The Extra Ordinary Meridians

In addition to the meridian systems there are some important areas in the body where the meridians interact to form major energy areas. These are termed Dantien, and the most notable ones are in the hara, and the sacrum areas. At these positions, an area can be marked out where the major tsubos form an area (roughly triangular in shape) encompassing the torso. For this reason these areas are powerful energy centres, and many practices, such as those involved in the martial arts will maintain a focus on these energy areas. Some have suggested that the Dantien correspond to the chakras, with the lower Dantien relating to the base chakra and it's associated aspect of the aura.

Human Energy   by   Dr Jarrod Hollis

Indian Approaches to Energy
The Nadis

Indian approaches to Energy

Concepts of human energy in India have connections with Tantric, Yogic and Hindu traditions. The word tantra means loom and depicts the way that the universe is connected into a whole and the weaving of a spiritual tradition and philosophy. From these underlying principles, healing systems such as Ayuveda have emerged. In many ways, other systems, such as the Tibetan approaches to energy, closely follow those emerging from India.

According to Indian traditions, the human physical body is seen as a cosmos of energy. The cosmos is considered to have evolved from prakrti, which has three qualities that correspond to matter (tamas), energy (rajas) and consciousness (sattva). These gunas integrate in different proportions to yield physical form, energy (force) and consciousness. There is also an energy or potential for consciousnes, known as kundalini.

The universe is a creation which emerges with the combination of the Hindu deities Shiva and Shakti. Shiva is the male principle and is said to be pure consciousness without form, and the divine potential within us all. Shiva is considered to be present at the crown. Shakti is the female principle, and the creator and mother of the universe. The word Shakti means "to be able" or "to have power". From Shakti, maya (the substance of the physical world) is created. You could think of maya as a projection of consciousness that manifests the physical. Shakti is present in the area of the base chakra.

There is a union between Shiva and Shakti, such that these energy forms move toward one another, Shiva, descends towards earth whilst Shakti ascends towards heaven. The descending current takes pure consciousness without form and gradually as the energy travels downwards it becomes denser top finally manifest on a physical level. In contrast the energy from Shakti starts as a dense form and then gradually rises to become finer and lighter and ends in a formless universality.

This energy travels through the body along specific pathways or energy conduits termed nadis. There are a number of major central nadis that form a vertical pathway. The centre channel is known as the sushumna. The sushumna (aka the Brahma nadi) is a major channel, that contains other, more subtle central channels, known as the vajra, and the chitrini or chitra and the canalis centralis nadis. The sushumna is also known as the royal life force or royal pathway.

Two other channels run either side of the sushumna. These are the Ida and the Pingala. The Ida and Pingala are thought to be related to the sympathetic and para sympathetic nervous systems. This is particularly apparent when you consider their location and pathway along the spine. The Ida nadi commences at the right side of the coccyx and the Pingala at the left. The Ida finishes at the left nostril (or in some texts at the centre of the brow) and the Pingala finishes at the right side of the nostril (or centre of the brow). In contemporary descriptions, the Ida and Pingala take a spiral like route around the shushumna. Where the two nadis intersect, an energy vortex (chakra) occurs. Note however, that in the classical descriptions, the Ida and Pingala were not depicted as spiralling or intersecting, and were described as taking a route very similar to the inner bladder meridian found in Traditional Chinese Medicine. Nevertheless the central channels are perhaps some of the most important ones, as they fulfil major functions. These major nadis have a number of associations that are indicative of their active and passive qualities. The Ida is termed chandra or moon nadi and conveys lunar energy.

The Main Nadi's:
The Sushumna, (show in white) with the Ida and tha Pingala
(shown in blue and red). The central sushumna connects each
chakra and the Ida and the Pingala cross over and intersect the
Sushumna.

It is the feminine principle and the channel of physical-emotional energy. The Pingala is termed the surva or sun nadi, conveying solar energy. It is the masculine principle of intellectual-mental energy.

As the flow of energy in the Ida and the Pingala are travelling in opposite directions, the energy starts to circle and form an energy vortex. This vortex is the basis of the major chakras. This is why the major chakras are found along the sushumna, or central channel. A chakra is positioned where the sushumna junctions with other nadis.

Branching throughout the body there are many thousands of finer nadis. In fact there are as many as 72,000 nadis. It is interesting to note that, unlike the Traditional Chinese meridians, the nadis are not often documented in the limbs.

Some of the nadis appear to have a close correspondence to the meridians found in Traditional Chinese Medicine (TCM) whilst others have no correspondence. For example, the nadis called Gandhari and Hastijihva are closely related to the Ida. They flow beside the Ida and their position is similar and thought to relate to the Bladder meridian of TCM.

The Pusha is a nadi that runs behind the Pingala, and ends at the right eye. It is also thought to relate closely to the Bladder meridian of TCM. The Alambusa runs from the anus to the mouth and this nadi has a close correspondence to the conception vessel found in TCM.

Although it appears that some of the nadis have a close correspondence to the meridians of TCM, not all of them fit directly into the TCM system. For example, the Shura is a nadi that runs from the navel to the brow, and this does not correspond to any TCM meridian.

It is interesting to note that the symbol that is common in modern day healing is the caduceus. This symbol consists of two shakes that wind around a central pole or staff. It could be argued that this symbol is a modern copy of the three central channels that have just been described. Note the similarities of the winding channels and the caduceus with the double helix known to be found in the DNA of all life forms.

According to Indian (Hindu) cultures, source is Kundalini. The term Kundalini is derived from the Sanskrit meaning 'serpent energy'. For this reason, Kundalini is often portrayed as a serpent. Kundalini is the active energetic property, which functions under the direction of Universal Law. Kundalini has a function of recycling and directing life energy, and to differentiate this from shakti, one might consider it as an energetic potential or enlightening force. Kundalini has been characterised as a reservoir of creative energy. This energy potential of consciousness lies dormant at the base of the spine, and is considered to be dormant unless activated through spiritual practice such as meditation or yoga. The power of Kundalini is claimed to be awesome and beyond description (note the similarity here to the great void).

In the classical literature Kundalini is characterised as having three different forms: The first of these forms is universal para-kundalini. The second of these is a body-mind complex called prana-kundalini. The third of these is as consciousness form called shakti-kundalini which integrates the other two forms. The term kundalini is not only found in the Hindu tradition, but is used by occultists, due to its reference to potential power and force that resides in the base chakra.

Zone Theory

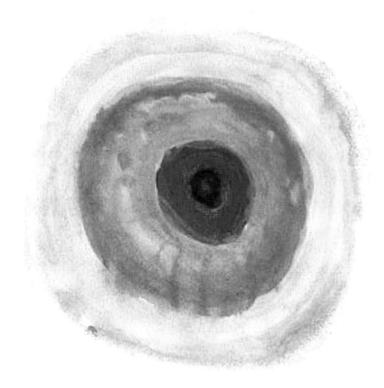

Zone Theory: A Western Approach to Energy and Health

In the West there are many different ideas about how the body can be encouraged to heal and balance through manipulating the bodies vital energy in some way. Nevertheless, after just a short examination, it is very clear, that the Western ideas on this area are no where near as established as those found in the East. Indeed, many of the therapies that have been formed in the UK, and the west are adaptations of the ideas from other cultures.

One theory and health system that does attempt to characterise energy flow in a novel way, without drawing pieces from other cultures is zone theory. Zone theory is the basis of the therapy reflexology.

Zone theory is a particularly interesting theory as it is perhaps one energy therapy the has its development in the West, rather than the East (although many books claim that reflexology originated in ancient Egypt India and China). However, this premise is a topic of current dispute.

We shall now consider zone theory and its original ideas, and then consider how (and if) this theory may relate to the other energy channels that we have discussed already.

Zone Theory and Reflexology

Reflexology is a method for activating the healing powers of the body and works with subtle energy flows, revitalizing the body so that the natural internal healing mechanisms of the body are activated to do their own work.

The basis of the therapy is zone theory and in its western form is attributed to an America doctor, Dr. William Fitzgerald. Fitzgerald found that pressure techniques could be put to a variety of uses, such as pain control, and emerging from his observations, Fitzgerald

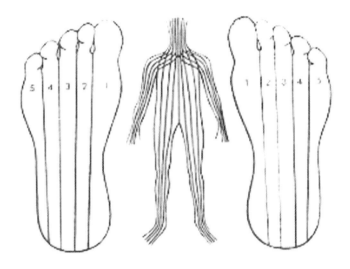

characterised the body into ten zones. The ten zones ran along the body lengthways from the tips of the toes to the top of the head.

Fitzgerald suggested that a body organ found within a certain zone was linked energetically to other areas within the same zone or channel. These zones were used by Eunice Ingram (1879-1974) who formed reflexology as we know it today. She found that the feet were particularly good areas to treat with pressure. Ingham gradually charted the areas of the foot to form the basic reflexology chart.

According to reflexology, energy travels through these zones. When the energy in a zone is balanced, the energy flows well. However, if the body contains any form of disharmony, the energy in the zones does not flow so well and blockages manifest. The flow of energy in the zones can be maintained and encouraged to flow by massaging the zones using pressure techniques. This balances the energy in the zones and encourages the body to heal and balance itself.

Reflexology is certainly a very popular therapy and therapists practice with great success. Nevertheless, there are a few issues regarding the nature of the five zones that remains hitherto unexplained.

Firstly, in reflexology, the nature of the energy flowing in the zones has not been characterised. It is simply labelled "universal energy". Often students and other therapists (and even in some books) term this Qi, or prana, but as our previous chapters have shown this is a gross generalisation and is not theoretically accurate.

Secondly, following on from this, many therapists and even some text books claim that the zones relate directly to the meridians. This is simply not the case. The zones do not have any direct correspondence to the meridians; certainly not to the classical (major meridians). I will illustrate this point. Take any meridian, for example the Gall Bladder meridian of the wood element. Now trace its pathway. You will see that the gall bladder meridian crosses literally all of the five zones, a number of times. This can be seen most clearly in the diagrams that follow.

The Gall Bladder & Liver Meridians of the Wood Element and the Five Zones of Reflexology Theory.

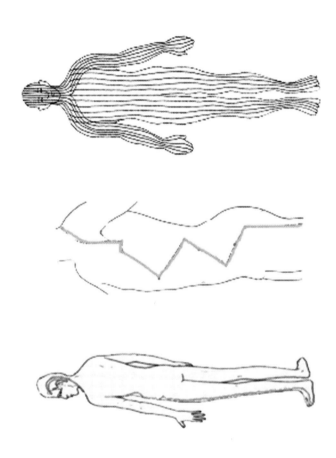

As can be clearly seen the gall bladder meridian zig-zags across literally all of the five zones. The liver meridian also crosses a number of different zones.

If we do this for each of the major meridians we can see that non of the meridians correspond to the five zones. Instead, the different meridians all cross a different number of the zones. There is no clear correspondence in the number of times or the ways that the meridians cross the zones.

There is also a further complication that clearly shows us that the zones and the major meridians show no direct correspondence. If we look closely at the diagram of the five zones we can see that the same five zones are found on the hands and the feet. This is not the case with the meridians. The hands and feet contain different meridians that belong to different elements.

You will recall, that the hand and arm contain the triple heater, the heart protector, the heart and the small intestine, the lung and the large intestine meridians. These correspond to the fire and metal elements. Now if we consider the legs and the feet, here we find the earth, water and wood elements, represented as the stomach and spleen, the kidney and bladder and the liver and gall bladder meridians.

It is therefore very clear that the hands and the feet contain classical meridians from different elements. If there was a direct correspondence with the meridians and the zones, we would find these meridians in both the limbs and in the same zones. This is not the case. Finally, it is often forgotten that according to TCM the meridians do not just channel Qi.

Another interesting issue regarding the zones is that theoretically pressure applied to any part of the zone, will balance energy within that zone. Nevertheless, it has often been observed and documented that working on the feet produces much better therapeutic responses than working elsewhere, such as the hands. A few hypothesis have been put forward to explain this such as: a) the hands are more mobile and so don't respond as well. b) the hands are smaller and the zones are closer together – this means that specific points on the zone are harder to locate accurately. c) the feet respond better to treatment as the body weight is carried through the feet due to gravity. This moves energy downwards, making the feet more responsive. We shall now consider how we might resolve some of these issues, and determine which of these explanations proves most adequate.

Renbardou Theory

The following theoretical ideas are the latest development of zone theory, proposed by Jarrod Hollis and Renée Tanner in 2003. Certainly the approach is perhaps the most clearly documented examination of zone theory.

We have termed the theory the Renbardou theory as the Ren is the first letters of Renee's name, but also, the channel Ren mai is central to out theory. Bardo is taken from Tibetan, which means transformation. Hence, Renbarou theory is a transformation and development of the old zone theories, to provide a more detailed account of the five zones.

Certainly it is clear that the zones do not correspond to any of the 12 major meridians, and furthermore the energy that flows in the zones can not be considered to be the same as Qi or prana; in the western approaches we have mind and brain, and thus our mental processing is not considered to be distributed around our body.

According to the Renbardou theory, the zones are channels in their own right. They are not the same as the 12 major meridians in any form. Instead according to the law of physics we can see that the five zones occur energetically as a result of the physical forces. They are mirrors of the central channel the ren mai and the du mai, or the shushumna. This is clear for a number of reasons. Firstly, it is this central channel that is universal to all of the approaches. If you remember all approaches indicate that it is this central pathway that is the most important. In the Hindu ideas the sushumna is where the kundlini rises, and in the Tibetan approaches it is the central channel, or the royal force, that integrates the elements with consciousness to allow life in the material world. In TCM, the central ren mai and du mai are the sea of all yin and yang for the whole body.

Renbardou
Theory of the Five Zones

In the diagram opposite the pink line represents the central nadi. The central nadi is the sea of all yin and yang in the body: the royal force. Gravity pulls energy downwards, and at right angles to the central channel. This creates mirrors of the central nadi that run vertically through the body.

As each zone is a mirror of the central channel, and not part of one of the 12 major meridians, it relates to organs and body structures within the same zone.

As the zone is product of the central channel it integrates all aspects of human energy, both the spiritual component and the more physical component.

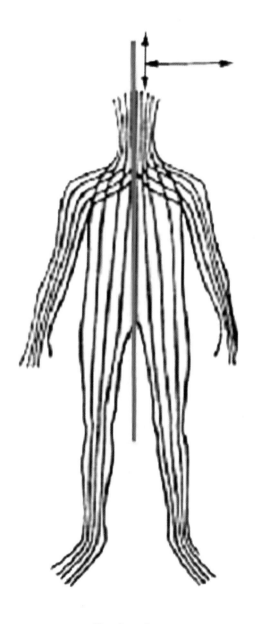

Renbardou
Theory of the Five Zones

The interesting conceptual issue here is that to claim that the five zones originate from the central nadi, indicates why they can be found on each side of the body and in both the arms and the legs. The central channel contains both yin and yang, and all of the elements. Therefore if the zone is a mirror of the central channel or nadi each zone contains and represents all of the elements, in both yin and yang forms.

You might ask whether it is possible that the central channel can form mirror like reflections that we think of as the five zones. Certainly, if we consider views from some other energy therapies, and from physics we can see how and why the zones are formed.

Robert Zeigler is an energy therapist in the USA. According to Zeigler, The most energy systems connect vertically with the source. In this case Zeigler attributes source to earth and sky, and suggests that this same basic pattern or structure is found with all life forms. However, Zeigler claims that human energy forms a horizontal pattern as humans were separated from source a long time ago. Zeigler maintains that the result of this separation is that the physical emotional and mental aspects of the human are separated from their spiritual body.

Zeigler goes onto explain that in a horizontal system, the crown and the root chakra open upwards (have a vertical orientation) whereas the other chakras have a horizontal orientation.

This can provide on way of explaining the existence of the five zones. The energy has a vertical origin, but expresses outwards (horizontally). This horizontal momentum creates what we consider to be the five zones.

This is not the only theoretical idea to explain how the five zones can be derived from the central nadi.

Thomas Jacobs, is another contemporary energy therapist whose ideas on energy can be used to help us explain how the central main nadi can be mirrored into five zones. Jacobs asserts that gravity is strongest force that affects the human body and has formulated ideas on how gravity affects subtle human energy.

According to Jacobs the energetic effects are all due to the fact that a mass moving at right angles to the pull of gravity creates a field of magnetic force. As the human body moves through the earth's gravitational pull, the subtle energy in the body is made to flow.

If we apply this idea to human energy, the body is upright, and energy is pulled downwards, in the central channel. As the body is never completely static the energy is pulled at right angles outwards to form the five energy zones. Subtle energies flow along these zones in a vertical direction.

Jacobs suggests that one can experience this directional flow of subtle energy personally. You will notice that if you perform an energy awareness exercise and move your hand towards and away from you can sense the energy much more than when you move your hand in a vertical direction.

Finally what about the nature of energy that flows through the zones? Is it Qi or prana? When we discussed the nature of Qi in TCM we saw that qi was a force like energy, but that this was not the same as the Shen, Po or Hun etc which were other forms that were differentiated and located in specific parts of the body. To label the energy that is being expressed in the zones as Qi is therefore not theoretically correct. According to the Renbardou theory, the zones are a mirror of the central nadi. It is therefore perhaps more appropriate to term the energy form prana, however note that the term prana does not contain the subtle qualities, that were discussed when the Indian ideas were considered.

Personally, I feel it is not viable to use terms from other cultural systems, unless they are being used in an appropriate context. I would suggest that as the zones carry an energy that does not differentiate physical and spiritual aspects but more of a general form of energy, it is more appropriate to form a term such as universal energy, without directly claiming it is the same as energy from another cultural system.

Summary of the Renbardou theory

Renbardou theory is a detailed account of the five zone theory. According to this theory, the five zones originate form the central energy channel or nadi. This channel is of prime importance in all cultural explanations of human energy.

Energy is subject to physical properties and to the effects of gravity; the energy travels in a vertical direction. However, due to the nature of the human energy system, these forces also pull the energy at right angles. This forms energetic patterns or mirrors of the central channel, which run vertically through the body. These areas are what we term zones.

As the energy is travelling in vertical lines, organs and body structures within the same zone only, can be activated at points found within the same zone.

The feet are the area of the human body that are most responsive to reflex zone treatment. This occurs for a number of reasons. Firstly, gravity is responsible for the energy zones forming and gravity is acting on the whole body weight through the feet. Therefore this makes the feet particularly sensitive. Secondly, the foot area is the bodies physical and symbolic link with the earth. If one considers the foot chakra, this is where the body connects with the earth element. Recall that this chakra allows the consciousness to manifest in physical form. It is no surprise that in respect of zone therapy, working on the feet, rather than some other area, has a strong effect on subtle energies.

Renbardou theory acknoweldges that the energy in the zones is derived from the cental nadi, but is not the same as Qi or indeed prana. The energy that flows in the zones is generalised and houses all aspects of the human energy field: both a spiritual and a physical aspect. Therefore we simply term this energy form *universal energy* or *generalised qi*.

Conclusions

In the previous chapters, we have considered different cultural explanations of human energy. This final section, provides a summary of the main issues.

Is clear that the Indian, Tibetan and Chinese approaches provide detailed explanations of human energy; not only the energy field itself, but its origins, and how the energy manifests and flows within and around the physical form.

The qualitative research conducted by myself and Renée Tanner identifed that people attempt to characterise human energy as an underlying driving force or power. They also relate this force to a spiritual component that they associate with human consciousness.

It was clear that people also identify that they see human energy and the energy from the environment as interdependent. The results of the qualitative analysis show striking similarities with the principles of yin-yang, even though the people that were questioned had little or no knowledge of the laws of yin-yang.

Each of the different cultural explanations placed emphasis on a different aspect of the person; the Tibetans and Indian approaches emphasise the connection with the spiritual and internal aspects and identify that these are important for health and well being.

In TCM the emphasis is on how one interacts with the environment, and how external forces (the environment, the weather etc) and internal forces (the emotions) are important precursors for well being. All of these explanations adhere to the laws of yin-yang.

These theories also take great care to detail the different aspects of the human energy; both the force aspect (e.g. qi) and the spiritual aspect (e.g. the shen, the hun).

The Western and New age approaches have borrowed many of the Indian and Chinese ideas and the concept of the chakras is one example. Many new therapies also characterise the human aura. This is in essence a generalisation of the different aspects that have been founded in the traditional Asian ideas.

Few of these new generation approaches have depicted detail. Indeed two aspects that are often missed out or glossed over in the Western/ New age approaches are the spiritual/consciousness aspect and the routes of the energy pathways themselves.

One may argue that the ideas on the human aura capture the spiritual aspects of the whole being. Nevertheless, in this material it is not clear how this relates to the mind or how this energetic quality is integrated into the physical. It is also not clear, why it stays around the physical form, or how it arrived their in the first place! I am sure that many people who might read this might present some theories about this, but the point is that compared to the Indian, Tibetan and Chinese theories, this aspect is not well defined or characterised.

One further point that has been neglected is detail regarding how the energy flows through the body in terms of channels. One exception to this is zone theory. Zone theory is a generalised theory that has placed an emphasis on how and where the energy flows through the physical body. Renbardou theory is the most recent development of zone theory. Renbardou theory indicates why the zones are in the positions they are, but also why the energy that flows within these zones is in a generalised form.

It is clear that one issue remains. What can one consider the most suitable theory to use as a basis for therapy? Actually the answer is very simple…..it depends on the person and the condition that is being treated. Certainly if someone responds well to any of the therapies then this is the most important aspect of the treatment – not how you try to intellectualise and explain the treatment results. Nevertheless, considering the way that people have described human energy in different way is important. It indicates the complexity of what is being dealt with. It is therefore no surprise, that sometimes people receive treatment, and the results are not as apparent as one would hope for. In this case, it is quite likely that something is being overlooked. Perhaps the therapist has missed something when performing the consultation. Perhaps something in the clients' lifestyle is counteracting the treatment? Perhaps the condition is very deep rooted and needs a more radical approach!

Certainly, human energy is powerful healing force, but remember that human energy is often termed *subtle energy* and unless the person is completely free from blocks, subtle energy will only work *subtly*. This takes time!

Human Energy   by   Dr Jarrod Hollis

Further Reading

Here are some other works that will give you more information and expand on some of the specific topics introduced in this book. I hope you will find them interesting.

Brennan, B., A. (1987) Hands of Light: A guide to healing through the human energy field.
Bantam Books
This book presents the classical commentary on the human aura, detailing the seven bodies. It is perhaps the most popular account of the human aura on which most other descriptions are based.

Gienger, M (1998).Crystal Power, Crystal Healing: the Complete Handbook.
Cassell
This is a beautifully written and illustrated book. I feel it is one of the best books on crystals I have seen.

Kaptchuk, T.,J (1983). Chinese Medicine.
Rider
One of the classic texts on traditional Chinese medicine.

Khenchen Thrangu Rinpoche (2004). Medicine Buddha teachings.
Snow Lion Publications.
A beautiful book on the history and practice of the Medicine Buddha sadhana.

Tanner, R. (1998). Reflexology: The Case History Book.
Douglas Barry Publications.
An interesting collection of case studies for those interested in reflexology.

Tanner, R. (2003). Step by Step Reflexology.
Douglas Barry Publications.
A classic no nonsense text for those wanting to practice reflexology. An informative guide and reference for the practitioner.

Index

A

B

C

Chi 24, 26, 96
chi 30
China 90, 124
Chinese 70
Christianity 18
Clairvoyance 52
coloured clouds 43
complimentary forces 66
complementary therapies 23
Conception Vessel 114
consciousness 28, 32
corporeal soul 98
Crown Chakra 51

D

descriptors 23
dhatu 93
DNA 122
Dorje Sempa 66
doshas 89
Du Mai 114
du mai 130
dysfunction 43

E

Earth Element 103
earth element 83
Egypt 22, 124
elan vital 30
electric charge 41
Electricity pylons 25
electron 30
Element Theory 70
emotional body 39
endocrine glands 48
energy 33
energy centres 46
energy vibration 39
energy vortices 46

higher chakras 48
Hindu 31, 34, 118
Hinduism 18
Hippocrates 70
hologram 49
humors 70
Hun 94

I

Ida 119
India 22, 90, 124
India and Tibet 86
Indian Elements 86
Indian head massage 17
indicator 33
innermost desires 54
integrated energy field 36
Islam 18

J

Jala 86
Jing 96

K

Kapha 87
Kashmir 32
ketheric body 40
Ki 96
Kidney Meridian 110
Kirlian Photography 41
Ko cycle 75
Kundali 31
Kundalini 31, 122
kundalini 118

L

La 94
Lama 66
Lapis Lazuli 91

Human Energy   by   Dr Jarrod Hollis

Other books by
Dr Jarrod Hollis

Available now:

Crystal Ayurveda

**Research Methods
for Complementary Therapists**

Coming soon:

**Anatomy & Physiology -
The Question & Answer Book**

Human Energy   by   Dr Jarrod Hollis

Human Energy   by   Dr Jarrod Hollis